"Are you going to search out my hidden depths?"

Calum asked Charlie. "And expose them for all to see? Is that what you're aiming to do to me?"

"Of course," Charlie said with wide-eyed innocence. "Didn't explain that early on?"

Calum shook his head. "You may have. But now—" he nodded toward the painting Charlie had been talking about "—I'm beginning to understand just a little, though, of course, I shall need a lot more tuition before I can even begin to grasp what you're trying to achieve. A lot more," he added in a low voice.

He moved nearer so their bodies were as close as possible without touching. Charlie sensed—knew— he wanted to touch her. She dropped her eyes and her pulse began to quicken. But did she want him to?

PORTRAIT OF A STRANGER

Helena Dawson

Harlequin Books

TORONTO • NEW YORK • LONDON
AMSTERDAM • PARIS • SYDNEY • HAMBURG
STOCKHOLM • ATHENS • TOKYO • MILAN

Original hardcover edition published in 1990
by Mills & Boon Limited

ISBN 0-373-17089-0

Harlequin Romance first edition July 1991

PORTRAIT OF A STRANGER

CHAPTER ONE

CHARLIE leant back in her corner seat with a sigh of utter satisfaction and closed her eyes, only to open them again almost immediately to glance sideways at the large parcel occupying the seat next to her. She rested her hand on it lovingly. What a day it had been! And what luxury to be travelling home first class! It might be an extravagance, but it wasn't every day you won five thousand pounds and she, Charlotte Flynn, winner of the Trevelyan Prize, had every right to indulge herself if she felt like it. In any case, she thought in added self-justification, the second-class compartments were already full to overflowing with tired shoppers and early commuters, and her precious package needed protection from the pushing throng of travellers. Didn't it deserve a bit of VIP treatment after the success it had brought her?

Success... Charlie considered the word carefully. Yes, she reckoned she could really say she had made it at last after all those years struggling to make ends meet and get her name known where it mattered.

She closed her eyes again and, as her thoughts drifted out into a future suddenly rosier than had ever seemed possible or probable, she was vaguely aware of hearing the guard's whistle and sensing the train begin to pull away...

'Oh!'

The train jerked violently to a stop, jolting Charlie back to earth, and instinctively she flung her arm

5

sideways to prevent her package being thrown to the floor. Outside on the platform she could hear a commotion of raised voices, angry and male, then the slamming of doors before the whistle blew again, and once more the train drew away from the station. Even before Charlie had time to settle down, the door of her compartment was slid abruptly back by a tall man who stood silhouetted against the light, hesitating, as though uncertain whether to commit himself to a compartment already occupied.

Something about his attitude and the impatience written on his face warned away even the tentative smile hovering on Charlie's lips, and she watched him from under her lashes as, his mind made up, he pulled off his coat and flung it on to the rack before dropping heavily on to the seat diagonally opposite from hers and opening his briefcase to extract a copy of the *Financial Times*.

He ignored Charlie completely, not acknowledging her presence by so much as a glance in her direction. She might have been invisible so far as he was concerned, buried behind the pink pages of his paper.

Charlie felt unaccountably piqued by the man's rudeness. She knew well enough that commuters made it almost a matter of honour not to speak to one another, but just for once couldn't he have made an exception to the unwritten rule? Couldn't he *see* what a special day it was for her and vouchsafe her just a token smile?

Evidently not. Charlie glared her annoyance, finding herself staring at him more intently than she might otherwise have done. There was something about her fellow traveller that intrigued her, and not only his undeniable good looks... There was an air of authority in his demeanour, almost like a pent-up energy bordering on aggression. Whatever it was, Charlie felt the old familiar itch tingling in her fingers and after only a moment's hesitation she reached surreptitiously for the sketch-book she always carried with her, even today.

With swift and assured lines the outline of the bent head appeared on the paper, then she blocked in the lines of the powerful body almost but not quite relaxed in his corner seat, the long legs stretched out before him. Charlie tried to capture the air of self-confidence that emanated from him, and the strength of the muscles that the smooth, expensive cloth of his suit couldn't altogether disguise.

Then, as the train swerved, the late afternoon sun slanted in through the window, making Charlie catch her breath. If only she had her paints! Until that moment she hadn't realised what a startling auburn his hair was, deep copper, almost glowing against the white cloth of the headrest. She screwed up her eyes against the sunlight, trying to analyse the colour, mentally mixing her palette—umber, sienna, yes, and alizarin crimson with glints of warm yellow... then add some dark, rich blue for the shadows under the square jaw and where the hairline met the curve of his neck...

She liked the shape of his hands, too, as they flicked the pages of his paper, the strong, square-tipped fingers that played with his pen as he made notes in the margin. But what colour were his eyes? It was so frustrating not to be able to see them under the heavy lids. Her own eyes moved rapidly from figure to sketch-book and back as her fingers deftly added a line here, a smudge of shading there, till the whole image began to take on a life of its own.

A surge of exhilaration swept through her with the realisation that this could be the start of something she could develop into a really exciting work back home in her studio. And she could add that mysterious reflection in the window behind his head—even a title sprang to mind. She would call it *Portrait of a Stranger*.

'Do you mind?'

Startled, Charlie's head jerked up, her eyes wide with surprise.

'I'm sorry?'

'I said, do you mind? Maybe I should have been more explicit. Do you mind not staring at me? I don't like it.'

There was no doubt now about the colour of his eyes. They were brown, dark brown, glaring at her from under straight uncompromising brows.

A faint blush stained Charlie's cheeks.

'I'm sorry,' she smiled contritely. 'It's a bad habit of mine, I'm afraid, but I do find faces fascinating. I'm a portrait painter, you see, and so I suppose you could say faces are my trade.' Shyly she proffered the sketchbook, but the tightening of his lips warned her quickly to draw back her hand.

'I see.'

Any hope Charlie might have cherished that her confession would win him over was swiftly crushed by the coldness in his voice. The stranger raked her slight figure briefly, as clearly unimpressed by her appearance as by her explanation.

'Well, I'd be grateful if you wouldn't practise on me. If I want my portrait painted——' he paused, frowning, as though an unwelcome thought crossed his mind '—I can afford the best.'

His brows lifted contemptuously as his angry eyes met hers before, quite deliberately, he turned away from her, shaking the pages of his paper with an irritation that nearly rent them apart.

Charlie's jaw dropped as she gazed back at him, wide-eyed with amazement that anyone could be so rude.

'Pardon me for breathing,' she muttered under her breath, still glaring at him, then, as he shifted his position slightly, she noted the deep lines etched between his eyes and beside the firmly compressed mouth.

Supposing he had had a bad day, and had been hoping for an hour or two's peace and quiet settled into his corner... maybe it had been a bit of a liberty to take advantage of him like that.

She could afford to be charitable, after all.

'The best,' she mused. With the cheque for five thousand pounds here in her bag, and beside her her own self-portrait which she had entered for the prestigious Trevelyan Prize and which the judges had seen fit to consider the best of all the entries, perhaps it wasn't too far-fetched, or vain, to think she might well be one of 'the best' in the not too far distant future.

She smiled contentedly to herself. She mustn't let one man's irritation spoil what had up till now been a marvellous day.

She stared out of the window, shutting him out of her line of vision and out of her mind as she consciously turned her thoughts to all that had happened to her over the past few hours, ever since she'd left Cambridge for the award-winning ceremony in London.

It had been fun, there was no doubt about it, being the centre of attraction, interviewed by the Press and even filmed for local TV, before being lavishly wined and lunched with the other prize-winners. Everyone had been so kind, praising her painting, wishing her well for the future... the future! A deep sense of pure joy spread through her and Charlie gave a little sigh of utter

happiness, quite lost on the stranger opposite, as a smile
curved her lips.

After all those years of taking any job she could get
just to have enough to live on: painting pictures of
people's houses, children, even dogs! Babysitting,
working in pubs, cleaning houses and offices . . . and all
that might, should, be coming to an end with the winning
of the Trevelyan Prize.

Charlie shut her eyes against the sun which had slowly
moved across the compartment as the train changed
direction, and, unbidden, another face swam before her
mind's eye, as unlike the one she'd been studying so
intently only minutes before as it was possible to imagine.

Thin, dark and forever mercurial, David seemed to
be grinning at her, but whether from pleasure at her
success or in mockery she couldn't tell. She could see
those bright blue eyes, the wide, laughing mouth, and
could hear his voice, as clearly as though he were beside
her.

'Come with me, Charlie. Let's conquer the world
before old age sets in and we have to settle down! There's
so much to see, we haven't begun to live yet!'

He had had this great idea of travelling where the fancy
took them, painting on pavements, doing quick portraits to keep body and soul together, and Charlie had
been tempted.

'Come on, Chas, it's now-or-never time.' He'd looked
at her quite gravely for someone who never took anything seriously except his work. 'I'm going, I've made
up my mind, and if you decide to stay . . .'

There'd been no need to elaborate. Charlie had had
no doubts that, if she stayed behind, their relationship,
their loving, stormy, exciting relationship, would be over.
She loved Dave, she had had no doubt of that, but deep

down she had known her needs were different. She'd wanted a secure base from which to work, not the nomadic existence that beckoned David.

She'd spent sleepless nights and agonising days trying to make up her mind, which in the end had been made up for her. Waking early one morning she'd found a note by the bed.

'Have taken the plunge to put us both out of our misery. See you around. Love, Dave.'

Had he despised her for staying behind? She couldn't tell from the occasional postcard, and he never gave any hint of whether or when he might return. She still missed him, but the pain of his abrupt departure had been eased by time and hard work, especially since she'd decided to enter her self-portrait for the Trevelyan Prize.

Charlie lost herself in a confused daydream and fell into a doze, only waking when they slowed down just outside Cambridge.

She watched through half-closed eyes as her fellow passenger glanced impatiently at his watch—gold, slim and clearly very expensive, Charlie noted—before packing away his paper and clicking the briefcase shut. Before the train was even in the station, he'd gone out into the corridor without so much as a nod in Charlie's direction, and as soon as the train had stopped she heard the door slam against the side of the carriage and had a final glimpse of the tall figure striding past her window and out of her life.

'Good riddance!' she muttered as she collected up her belongings, then put him resolutely from her mind, for now she had more important things to take care of.

There was only one way of getting herself and her precious parcel back to her flat and that was by taxi.

'I could get used to this high life with no trouble at all,' she confessed with a grin to her landlady, Annie, who was waiting all agog to hear how she'd got on. 'First-class travel all the way really suits me!'

Charlie heaved the heavy picture through the door and kicked off her shoes in the middle of the hall before starting up the two flights of stairs to her top-floor studio flat.

'Come and have a cuppa in the kitchen and tell me all about it. The kids are glued to the telly, and Don's dining in College, so I've got a few blessed minutes to myself,' Annie invited her.

'That'll be lovely—thanks.' A cup of tea and someone to share her reminiscences with suddenly seemed what Charlie wanted most in the world. She *was* lucky, she thought for about the hundredth time, to have found a home with Don and Annie, a university lecturer and his teacher wife, and since the day she'd moved into their house she'd always felt she was more than just a tenant.

How many cuppas she'd had at Annie's kitchen table over the past three years Charlie couldn't have said, she thought gratefully as she made her barefoot way back downstairs after trudging up with her painting. She collected her shoes and padded out to find her landlady sitting half-hidden as usual behind a huge pile of exercise books. 'Kettle's just boiled,' she said. 'Fill the pot, there's a love. Now, what have you been getting up to today?'

Charlie brought the teapot over and flopped down to join her. 'It's been an incredible day, Annie, I can't tell you. I'm still all in a whirl, so much has happened.' She grinned suddenly and waved a lordly hand over the table. 'Actually, you're very lucky to have me to make the tea for you. I'm a star now, I hope you realise, and I wouldn't have demeaned myself doing such a menial task for anyone but you.'

Annie pulled a face and poured out the tea as she waited for Charlie to come back to earth and fill her in with all the details. When she had finished she smiled and reached out to pat Charlie's hand.

'I'm very glad for you, my love. You've worked hard, and you've got the talent too. You deserve all the success that's coming to you.'

A wave of affection swept over Charlie as she met Annie's sympathetic smile.

'I couldn't have done it without you,' she told her gratefully. 'All those times when I was on point of giving it all up and you told me not to be so silly...not to mention subsidising me. I know you don't charge me as much as you should. Oh, that reminds me...'

Charlie scrabbled in her pocket and brought out a cheque. 'This is all my arrears up to date, plus a couple of weeks in advance,' she added with a grin. 'I'm rich enough to settle all my debts now.'

Annie took the cheque and smiled cheerfully. 'We always knew you'd make it. We'll be able to cash in on your success soon—showing people round the flat where the great Charlie Flynn began her career.'

They both laughed, then Annie leant her elbows on the table and rested her chin on her cupped hands.

'And what about the chairman of the sponsoring company, the man you're going to be painting? Just your average middle-aged grey-haired tycoon, is he?'

Charlie frowned. 'I never did get to meet him. They said he was away at a meeting, so I've got to ring to make an appointment to see him and fix up the details...pity, though, it'd have broken the ice, meeting him at the ceremony instead of alone in his office.'

*   *   *

A few days later, doing her best to exude an air of businesslike professionalism in spite of the whole cloud of butterflies fluttering round her stomach, Charlie presented herself at the reception desk of Sutherland Associates. She swallowed. This was it, crunch time, the beginning of a whole new life.

'My name's Charlie Flynn,' she told the elegant receptionist, 'and I have an appointment with the Chairman, Mr Calum Sutherland. I was told to ask for his secretary—Judy Bannister?'

A scarlet-tipped hand gestured towards the soft leather sofa in the corner.

'Please take a seat, Miss Flynn. Miss Bannister will be with you shortly.'

It was only then that Charlie wondered whether she should have announced herself as Charlotte. It did have a more sophisticated ring to it than Charlie, and it was certainly more formal. Still, she shrugged, Charlie's what I'm called, and it's too late now.

She sat down and tried to compose herself for the interview.

'Miss Flynn?'

Charlie turned to face a pretty girl, maybe a year or two older than her own twenty-four years, who was watching her expectantly.

'Yes, I'm Charlie Flynn. You are...?'

'Judy Bannister, Mr Sutherland's secretary. He is expecting you, if you'd like to follow me.'

Charlie did her best to quell a surge of apprehension as she followed Judy Bannister into the lift and then along a thickly carpeted corridor to a door leading into a large, comfortably furnished office where another girl was busily typing. She looked up and smiled at Charlie.

'This is my office,' Judy Bannister explained, 'and that's my assistant, Sue. Mr Sutherland's office is through there...' She pointed at an inner door, then pressed a button on the intercom.

'I have Charlie Flynn with me now, sir.'

'Come in, please, Judy.'

Judy opened the door to the Chairman's sanctum and ushered Charlie in, then turned and left them alone.

'Good morning, Mr Sutherland. I'm Charlie...oh!'

Her heart bounded wildly as the tall figure staring out the window turned to face her, powerfully built, muscular and strikingly auburn-haired. Piercing brown eyes met hers in total disbelief as he halted abruptly in his tracks.

Charlie matched his stare for what seemed an eternity while a welter of emotions cascaded through her brain.

The stranger on the train was a stranger no longer. She had thought that she had obliterated the memory of his dismissive treatment of her in her anxious preparations for today, but she'd been wrong. His words still rankled her mind. 'I can afford the best...' The sentence hung in the air between them in the long, awkward silence which he was the first to break as he moved with determined steps to sit at his desk as though anxious to put a physical barrier between them.

'You're a girl,' he observed bluntly. 'I wasn't expecting that.'

His eyes narrowed as they swept her slight form, clearly as unimpressed by what they saw as they had been on their previous meeting. 'I thought Judy said "Charlie" Flynn. An unusual name for a girl, surely?'

Charlie felt a flush creeping up her neck, matching her rising temper. This man seemed to have a gift for making her angry, but this time she was determined not to be outfaced. Her name had nothing to do with him.

'Charlotte, actually, but I'm always known as Charlie. And I can't help my sex,' she added tartly.

If she was expecting an apology she was to be sadly disappointed, but Charlie gave Mr Calum Sutherland no opportunity to insult her further as she pressed on with the initiative.

She forced a radiant smile which seemed momentarily to take him aback, and she thrust out her hand towards him.

'I'm very glad to meet you at last, Mr Sutherland— or should I say "again"?'

She felt her fingers being taken, almost reluctantly, in an unexpectedly firm grasp by a hand warm and hard, to which she instinctively responded, her eyes widening in pleased surprise, but no answering smile lit the cold eyes.

'Miss Flynn,' Calum Sutherland acknowledged briefly, then dropped his hand. He motioned her to one of several armchairs set round a small table, but Charlie paused before sitting down as she took in the spectacular panorama visible through the wide window. She turned back to the chairman, forgetting in her enthusiasm whom it was she was addressing.

'What a stunning view!' she exclaimed. 'If this were my office I don't think I'd ever get any work done at all!'

From her vantage-point high up over the Thames, Charlie could see the river winding away in both directions—a silver ribbon threading through its bridges with boats plying busily up and down like motorised toys.

Beyond stretched London, quiet and dignified now the din and bustle were out of sight and earshot. Charlie felt literally out of this world, entranced by the view, but behind her came an impatient sigh.

'I'm sorry, Miss Flynn, but I am a busy man, and I have a meeting in...' he glanced at the gold watch encircling his wrist '... precisely twenty-two minutes, so I suggest you come to the point.'

Charlie sat with neat precision on the edge of her chair, keeping her back straight in an effort to add inches to her comparatively insignificant height, and fixed her eyes steadily on his face.

'I am a portrait painter,' she began, but Calum Sutherland interrupted her with an impatient gesture.

'So you told me,' he interposed, looking not exactly overjoyed at the memory. But Charlie persevered doggedly, determined not to be put off.

'I am here as winner of the Trevelyan Prize which your company so generously sponsored this year——' she flashed him a smile '—and, in case you have forgotten, part of the first prize is a commission to paint the portrait of the chairman of the sponsoring firm, which, of course, will be yourself.'

A spasm crossed the handsome features. Calum Sutherland was not used to being held to account for absent-mindedness, and, as she noticed it, a sense of utter inadequacy swept over Charlie. Then, just as she was about to despair of the whole undertaking something like a miracle occurred. The stern expression on Calum Sutherland's face softened, just a fraction.

'I think some coffee would be a good idea,' he announced surprisingly. Charlie followed him with her eyes as he got to his feet to go over to the door. Every inch of him spoke of success, from his highly polished shoes and beautifully tailored suit to the spotless white shirt beneath. The only incongruous note was struck by that unruly crown of thick, coppery hair which, along with his name, surely belonged more to a Scottish laird than a city tycoon. Again Charlie's fingers itched for her paints...she dropped her gaze as he returned to the chair facing her.

'I should apologise,' he said stiffly, as though it were a novel experience. 'This meeting I'm due to attend is rather important; also——' he hesitated, meeting Charlie's gaze with a bleak expression '—quite frankly, I'm not really in the least interested in having my portrait painted by you or anyone else.'

Charlie began to feel utterly deflated. This was turning out to be quite the most depressing interview she'd had in any circumstances. The whole thing was a complete waste of time for both of them. She might as well pack up and go home now.

'It was my uncle's idea, you see,' Calum Sutherland went on, 'sponsoring the Prize and so on. He would have really relished the idea of commissioning a young artist—you, as it turned out...'

'Couldn't I paint him instead?' Charlie asked hopefully, grasping eagerly at anything that would get her—and Calum Sutherland—out of the impasse they found themselves in. 'I don't suppose it would matter to the organisers, especially if it was your uncle who agreed to the sponsorship in the first place.'

Calum Sutherland shook his head.

'Not unless you're willing to go to New Zealand to do it. He's gone out there to live with his daughter and her family. No—I'm afraid you're stuck with me.'

Judy Bannister arrived at this point with the tray of coffee. She poured out two cups then left them together, murmuring something about the meeting in ten minutes. The chairman nodded, and Charlie began to feel desperate. Nothing had been settled and time was slipping away.

She took a quick gulp of the coffee, set her cup down on the table, then rummaged in her bag for her sketch-book. She sat forward on the edge of her chair and held it out to Calum Sutherland.

'Look, these are what I did in the train—and you were quite right, it was an intrusion of your privacy, but taking quick notes like that is second nature to me, and I thought maybe I could work them into something rather interesting.' She coloured slightly. 'The way you were sitting in the corner, with the light coming through the window...' Her voice trailed away as Calum Sutherland flicked through the pages of drawings, frowning, and when he came to those of himself he raised his eyebrows.

'I wasn't aware I looked so forbidding,' he mur-mured, then looked Charlie straight in the eye. 'I have to tell you I don't know a great deal about art—you'll find me a very unsympathetic subject, I'm afraid.'

'You didn't even look at the entries for the Prize, did you?' Charlie took sudden courage from his last remark. Was he at last admitting defeat and agreeing to model for her? 'Otherwise you might have recognised me in the train—from my self-portrait—and you'd have known the winner wasn't a man.'

Calum Sutherland shook his head. 'As I said, I'm just not interested. I have too many things on my mind at present, and I knew I couldn't be there for the prize-giving ceremony, so it seemed a waste of time even to pretend I was—interested, that is. I'm sorry, it must sound very rude, but I find it's best to be honest, then no one is labouring under any false pretensions about me.'

'Might I make a suggestion?'

The dark eyes shot up again, and Charlie guessed that having anyone, particularly young and female, stand up to him was something outside his normal experience, but then she was in a privileged position, not being in his employ or in any way dependent on him for her livelihood. She could afford to take the risk in treating him as a normal human being. She, too, could be honest.

'As your time is limited, and clearly you are a very busy man, why don't I go ahead and work up some ideas from these sketches, and bring them back for your approval? You could decide which one you prefer, consult your wife, perhaps, and then we can arrange some longer sittings. Those will be essential, I'm afraid.'

Calum Sutherland shrugged his broad shoulders. 'I suppose so,' he said without enthusiasm, and his eyes glinted a warning. 'And for your information, although I don't see that it is any business of yours, I have no wife to consult. Marriage is another luxury my schedule cannot afford.'

Charlie was appalled to sense an unwelcome flutter in the region of her heart at the discovery that he was unmarried. What was it to her? If he were the last man on earth she would want nothing to do with him once this disagreeable assignment was over and done with— and the sooner the better so far as she was concerned. Desperation lent her courage as she saw him look at his watch again.

'Please, Mr Sutherland. This situation hasn't been of my making. I entered the competition in good faith...and it means a lot to me, this part of the Prize, even more than the money, since the portrait is guaranteed a place in next year's Young Painters Exhibition at the Hayward, and with luck that will bring other commissions...at least, that's the idea,' she ended faintly.

Calum Sutherland considered her in silence for a moment, then held out the sketch-book which he still had in his hand. Charlie reached out to take it, and as she did so became aware of a resistance in the grip of the strong, square-tipped fingers which forced her, almost against her will, to raise her eyes to his.

'You're quite a remarkable young woman,' he said surprisingly with what might have passed for a note of approval in his voice. He made no attempt to relinquish his hold on the sketch-book, so that their hands were firmly linked together.

'I haven't been particularly polite to you——' and that's putting it mildly, Charlie thought in exasperation '—and most people would have been put off and given up trying to get their own way by now.'

'Is that what you hoped for?' Charlie demanded hotly. 'Because if you were, you tried it with the wrong person. I won that prize, fair and square, and if painting you is part of it——'

'—then I—we—shall have to make the best of it,' Calum Sutherland agreed with resignation. He let Charlie have her book back, but kept his eyes on her face. 'If I'm involved in a contract, Miss Flynn, I make sure it is honoured, whatever it is.'

'Even if it's something you don't want to do?' Charlie enquired, bending down to put away her pad.

'Particularly if it's something I don't want to do.' Charlie looked up sharply but there was no time to follow up this interesting revelation as an urgent reminder on the intercom brought Calum Sutherland to his feet, and he came round to the other side of his desk, gathering up some files in readiness for the meeting.

Charlie hadn't stood quite so close to him before, and his sudden proximity made her realise just how tall and powerfully built he was. Her slight five-foot-three-inch frame was dwarfed as he towered over her, his innate strength almost intimidating, and, more than that, he positively exuded an aura of uncompromising masculinity. As he moved past her to open the door she caught the scent of his aftershave, very faint, mingled with the indefinable and disturbing essence of the man himself. Her heart gave a slight jump, but she walked resolutely in front of him, straight to the door, where she paused, forcing herself to look him steadily in the face. She could see Judy Bannister watching him anxiously, hovering with papers in her hand.

'I'll be in touch, then, when I've worked out a few ideas. I'll do my best not to waste any of your time, though I shall need one or two longish sittings . . . but I dare say you'll find it possible to carry on normally while I'm working.'

'Normally?' The dark brows rose in disbelief. 'I could hardly "carry on normally" as you so disingenuously put it, with you scribbling away in a corner watching my every move. Still . . .' He glanced over at Judy Bannister and nodded briefly. 'I expect we'll come to some kind of mutually convenient arrangement. Just ring Judy when you're ready, and we'll see how it goes. Now, if you'll excuse me, I must go.'

Calum Sutherland held out his hand, and as Charlie put her own into it and felt the strong fingers tighten round hers she flushed involuntarily, this time in full view of that appraising stare.

She withdrew her hand quickly, biting her lip in annoyance at the treacherous response of her senses to his touch. She didn't even like the man, for goodness' sake, and he certainly hadn't given her any reason to.

'Goodbye, Mr Sutherland,' she said coolly. 'I'll ring Miss Bannister as you suggest, and thank you for your time . . . and the Prize,' she added almost as an afterthought. A touch of politeness never came amiss, even, or perhaps especially, in the face of the chairman's lack of interest.

Although, Charlie thought later, going over the interview as she travelled home—second class this time—he hadn't seemed quite so uninterested towards the end, once she had begun to stand up for herself and made him see her as a person with a mind and ideas of her own. That momentary note of approval in his voice hadn't just been a mere figment of her imagination, any more than the sudden gleam in his eye as he had taken note of her outburst of professional pride and forced a physical bond between them by holding on so firmly to the sketch-book...

Charlie put her hand to her cheek as if to recall the warmth his scrutiny had brought to her face, then dropped it quickly. Whatever was she thinking of? She must remain totally objective if she was to make a professional job of this assignment. Personal feelings, whether of dislike or something warmer—though she couldn't imagine that would be the problem—must be kept ruthlessly at bay, or the whole thing would be a disaster. It was one thing to try to probe beneath the surface of her sitter's character, to find out what made him or her tick, but quite another to get emotionally involved.

As though to prove her resolution, Charlie lifted her bag on to her knee and took out her sketch-book, flipping through the pages until she came to the drawings she had made of Calum Sutherland in the train.

What had he said? That she had made him look forbidding?

Charlie's brows knitted in a frown as she perused her work. Forbidding wasn't quite how she would describe that face...certainly forceful, domineering, even aggressive...

She got out her ballpoint and from memory began to make adjustments to the straight, firm lips, deepening the furrows which ran from nose to mouth, altering the shape of the nose a little. The eyes, dark and direct, she seemed to have caught exactly... She snapped the book shut, as her breathing altered in time with her quickening pulse. In spite of all her earlier resolve, she couldn't disguise the fact that it was not only as an artist that her senses stirred at the prospect of the hours she would need to spend trying to capture the structure of those clear-cut features on her canvas. The Trevelyan Prize was going to be a challenge in more ways than one.

CHAPTER TWO

THE following day Charlie began work in earnest on the preliminary work for the portrait of the chairman of Sutherland Associates. She studied all the sketches she had made, then tried out various ideas in charcoal on large sheets of paper. There was no point in committing anything to canvas at this stage. Even so, she couldn't resist mixing up some paints for a first attempt at capturing the tones of that amazing auburn head. His hair was such an unusual colour, really dark red, and Charlie knew it would vary according to the light and surroundings—she must make sure she got him to sit where the sun could strike those crimson glints which contrasted so markedly with the dark blue shadows where the hair grew thickest and where it met the pale skin of his forehead.

She would also have to discuss with him what he should wear.

Charlie grinned. She could imagine their conversation only too clearly. He wouldn't take kindly to any interference in his domestic affairs, she knew, but if she could just get him to see she was only doing her job... If there was one thing he did understand, it was work. Charlie had discovered that much about him, at least.

Almost subconsciously her hand guided the brush round the outline of his features, added mouth and eyes and then, instead of the city uniform of suit and shirt she had only seen him in, hinted at a green sweater against a landscape of bracken and moorland leading

away to a range of blue-misted hills, just a rough indication of the Scottish setting she was convinced must be
his natural background, especially with a name like his,
and that hint of a Scottish lilt in his voice, that soft rolling
of the 'r'. That was something she could talk to him
about during the sittings. However uncooperative he
might be, they couldn't remain in total silence all the
time. Charlie worked on, and it was only when the light
began to fade that she realised how long she had spent
on the painting she had begun purely as a self-indulgent
exercise.

She walked over to the far side of her studio to get a
better view. From the easel Calum Sutherland's face
stared back at her with familiar arrogance and with a
disdainful curl to his lip, but there was a liveliness in his
expression that Charlie could only hope she could
recapture when she came to paint him for real. There
was even a glint of humour in the brown eyes which she
couldn't remember actually noticing herself, but which
her artistic instincts had added with a kind of independent vision of the man's character. Disconcerted by
her own creative powers, Charlie began running her
fingers through her short, dark hair till it stood up in
spikes, as she gazed back at the romantic image of the
man she disliked so much and who had treated her with
nothing but discourtesy at both their meetings.

Nothing in life was simple, she mused, as she put her
brushes away. She had been so sure she felt nothing but
dislike for the man, and yet . . . and yet there had clearly
been some deep-hidden facet of his character which had
called up a subconscious response from her, and she
wasn't at all sure whether she welcomed the knowledge.

Charlie shook her head and turned the easel to the
wall. The implications of this painting were too worrying,

and she needed a clear head, without complications, to tackle the real task which lay before her.

She worked hard over the next few days, developing her brief sketches into a series of outline portraits of Calum Sutherland in a variety of poses—full-face, profile, head and shoulders—against different backgrounds, although she did not repeat the romantic setting of moors and hills. That particular image of him must be kept strictly private. She regretted even having painted it at all, for some reason she couldn't quite fathom.

When she felt she could do no more on her own, and now needed the subject himself to decide which of the several alternatives he preferred, she rang Judy Bannister to make another appointment.

'Mr Sutherland's very busy at present,' Judy informed her. 'He has a lot of very important meetings over the next few days, and I doubt whether he could fit you in for some time. Is it important?'

Fit her in! Important! Charlie seethed inwardly.

'Of course it's important,' she retorted, summoning up a tone of cold dignity from some reserve of professional pride. 'I wouldn't be ringing otherwise. I realise Mr Sutherland only has limited time at his disposal, but I do have a commission to paint his portrait, and I can't do it without some sittings.'

'Oh, dear...'

Judy Bannister's voice took on a desperate tone and Charlie immediately began to feel sorry for her. It couldn't be easy working for a man like that, keeping unwanted callers at bay, and at least she had been honest. Getting angry wouldn't help.

'Look, I know it's difficult, and I know he doesn't want his portrait painted either, but the sooner I can see him and organise the sittings, the sooner it'll all be over.

This time I only need a few minutes. He'll only have to make a couple of quick decisions and flick through his diary, and I'll be out. Promise.'

'Well...' The relief in the other girl's voice was obvious even over the telephone. Had she been told to be as obstructive as possible? Charlie wondered. The life of a struggling artist might be precarious, but at least it was an independent one, not subject to the whims and vagaries of a boss with more power than was good for him.

'What about Friday—he'll probably have about fifteen minutes between meetings, at about eleven o'clock, if you don't mind waiting? Will that do?'

It'll have to, Charlie thought resentfully. All that way and expense for just a quarter of an hour. She could see her five-thousand-pound prize money being gobbled up in train fares if he was going to ration out his time in such meagre bites.

She got to the office early that Friday and was quick to reassure Judy when she saw the anxiety on the other girl's face.

'Don't worry. I know it's not time yet, but I thought I might wait in Mr Sutherland's office and do a few drawings, just in case he decides he wants the office background. It'll save time in the end,' she added temptingly, noting Judy's hesitation, 'and you can keep your door open so as to make sure I don't go poking round where I'm not supposed to.'

Judy's face broke into a smile.

'Is mind-reading part of an artist's training? All right, it's probably as much as my job's worth, but I can't see any harm in it.'

Charlie insisted on leaving the communicating door open—the last thing she wanted was to get Judy into trouble—then arranged all the drawings she'd done round the office so that everywhere she looked she found Calum Sutherland's eyes staring at her. It was quite unnerving. Then, before settling down with her pad and pencil, she stood with her back to the window and gazed round the room, trying to absorb the atmosphere. It might only be an office, but even so, like any other room, it should be able to tell her something about the man who worked here, more than she had been able to grasp during her first interview.

It didn't take her long to realise that any insight into what made the chairman of Sutherland Associates tick wouldn't come from these surroundings. This room bore no stamp of any individuality in its décor or furnishings. Some firm of interior decorators had been given a free hand, and it had been left at that. The walls were a harmless shade of pale turquoise, echoed by deeper tones of the same colour in curtains and carpeting. The furniture was all modern and very expensive, from the hide chair in which she had sat on her earlier visit to the large desk which was positioned uncompromisingly in the centre of the room bare of any personal possessions whatever—no photographs, not even a pen. The obligatory prints and plants were large and costly too, but the whole room looked more like an advertisement in a glossy brochure than the working space for one particular man with his own tastes and preferences. It could belong to anyone.

Charlie had an overwhelming desire to spill out the contents of her bag all over the virgin expanse of desk-top, to fill the empty wall-space with an untidily over-flowing bookcase like the one in Annie's living-room. Her grin at the mental picture this notion conjured up changed quickly to a frown. Why should this man want to keep everything so clinically bare? Was he scared of leaving even a hint of his personality in this room, or simply too busy to take any interest in his surroundings? Still, if anyone could penetrate the wall of privacy he had built round himself, she would be in as good a position as anyone.

Charlie perched on the edge of the vast desk and began to draw quickly, adding notes on the paper to help her put in the colour back in the studio. That blue-green would make a good foil for the auburn head...

'I see you've made yourself at home, Miss Flynn.'

Charlie had been so intent on her work that she hadn't heard the chairman's arrival in the adjoining room, the brusque questioning followed by Judy's anxious explanation of Charlie's presence in his office.

Now, caught unawares, she flung her head up and found Calum Sutherland staring down at her from the doorway with deep displeasure burning in the dark brown eyes. His brows barred in an angry frown.

'I don't know what you imagine you're doing in my office, Miss Flynn, and alone... Miss Bannister had no right to let you in.'

He took a few steps towards her, the movement threatening in a man so big and powerful, and Charlie instinctively flinched away, angry at his belligerence and simultaneously with herself for allowing herself to be intimidated in this way. She had nothing to apologise for.

Her first instinct was to retreat into the corner, but that was the coward's way out. She slid slowly off the desk and remained standing, one hand resting lightly on the surface, and met his gaze with a steely glint in her eye which, had he known her better, might have set alarm bells ringing.

'And you have no need to be so aggressive, Mr Sutherland,' she proclaimed silkily, determined now to stand her ground. 'I was doing no harm here, I assure you, merely trying to do both of us a favour by working on some preliminary background. I thought this would save some of your most valuable time.'

She allowed herself a hint of irony which probably wasn't particularly wise, but the man's attitude had stung her into it. She held out the sketches towards him.

'See—drawings of your office, that's all. Nothing sinister about those, is there? Take them, go on.' She thrust the pad towards his unwilling hands. 'See for yourself. I know nothing of this financial world of yours, and I couldn't read a balance sheet to save my life—or maybe you think all this——' she waved her hand towards the drawings displayed all round the office '—is only a front, and I'm really working for the Press, or some rival concern, investigating insider dealing, or whatever it's called. Is that it?'

Calum Sutherland made no attempt to take the proffered sketch-book.

'No, of course it isn't.' His eyes swept her scornfully. 'The idea is ridiculous and you know it. Kindly credit me with some intelligence.'

With a few swift strides he moved to the chair behind his desk and sat down, motioning to Charlie to take the seat opposite.

'I just do *not* appreciate having strangers in my office alone and unsupervised, whatever reason they might think they have for being there. I should be grateful if you would remember that, should the occasion ever arise again.'

His mouth narrowed into a thin line, and Charlie suddenly felt very small. This room didn't need *things*, objects cluttering up the empty space. This man's over-powering personality was enough to fill it completely.

'Well, Miss Flynn, I haven't much time, so let us get down to business.' Restless fingers strummed on the desktop, and the copper hair, catching the sunlight, seemed to flame with the impatience Charlie sensed was simmering only just below the surface. She spared a thought for Judy Bannister and hoped she wouldn't suffer too much from allowing herself to be persuaded to break the rules on Charlie's behalf. Now, the precious minutes were ticking away, and she must broach the matter which had brought her here.

She cleared her throat nervously and saw Calum Sutherland's lips twitch in irritation.

'I've made some drawings of you in different poses...' Again she waved towards them. 'I thought you might like to choose the one you'd like me to work up into the finished portrait. And I need to discuss the setting...this room, maybe, which is why I wanted some time here,' she put in faintly, 'or your home, or even the view through the window. It's up to you.'

In the face of his patent disapproval, Charlie felt the words hurrying over themselves in her anxiety to get the interview over as quickly as possible, and her voice trailed away in a dismal diminuendo.

Calum Sutherland sighed.

'I told you when we last met, I believe, that I have no interest in this whole scheme and no desire to have my likeness preserved for posterity. All I want is for the whole tiresome business to be dealt with as quickly as possible.'

Charlie was furious to feel a pricking behind her eyelids, and bent to retrieve her bag to hide the tears from this man who appeared to be going out of his way to hurt her. The last thing she wanted was for him to pick up any weakness on her part—he clearly despised her enough already. She blinked the wetness away and raised her eyes to him in a level gaze.

'Would you like to look at the drawings now?' she asked quietly. 'Then perhaps we could arrange a time for your first sitting...it need not be very long,' she added hastily, forestalling the danger signals flashing from the dark eyes. 'Just half an hour or so, and I can easily sit over there while you get on with your own work.' Calum Sutherland slapped his hands down on his desk then got quickly to his feet to stride towards the first of Charlie's drawings. He frowned irritably.

'I suppose any of them will do, won't it?' His gaze swept unheedingly round before his attention was caught by the nearest of the drawings.

'You do seem to have a knack for capturing a likeness, Miss Flynn, I'll grant you that, so why can't I settle for any one of them—this one will do—have it framed, and call it a day, instead of putting us both through a lengthy experience neither of us will enjoy?'

'"A finished portrait" the Prize specifies,' Charlie reminded him firmly. 'These are only working sketches—a real portrait should bring out the real character of the sitter...the man behind the face.'

Calum Sutherland's strong jaw tensed.

'Fanciful artistic nonsense!' he muttered. 'The whole thing's a waste of time, if you ask me!'

Barbarian, Charlie accused him silently. Philistine! She glared at the broad back hovering over the portrait she herself thought the best and resented the care she'd expended on it. He wouldn't recognise a work of genius if it were handed to him, but she must remember that other people would see the finished painting, other people who would appreciate her talent and, hopefully, give her further commissions. This man was just a means to an end. She would *not* let him get to her.

The barbarian swung round to face her.

'Which do *you* think the best? You must have some preference.'

Charlie smiled demurely.

'It's not for me to say, Mr Sutherland. It's the client's decision that is important, and I am entirely in your hands.'

The dark brows lifted.

'Really?' Calum Sutherland asked sarcastically. 'It doesn't feel that way, I assure you. If the matter *were* in my hands...'

'...you'd wash them of the whole affair,' Charlie finished for him. 'I know. I'm very sorry, but it's not of my doing, and I'm not deriving a lot of satisfaction from it myself, if it's any consolation.' She found she was trembling from a combination of suppressed misery and anger, but he was not going to get the satisfaction of seeing how upset he was making her. Charlie clenched her hands into fists by her side while she watched him glancing impatiently from one sketch to another.

'You're not going to give me any help? Surely there must be one or two you're more pleased with than the rest? Perhaps one you feel you would enjoy developing into a finished picture?'

Charlie looked at him in some surprise. For somebody who up till now had shown a marked lack of sensitivity both towards people and art in general, that was a pretty perceptive remark.

'There is one,' she admitted slowly, 'but I shouldn't influence you.'

'I know, it's not for you to say. Really, Miss Flynn, you are most aggravating. This isn't a guessing game—

my time is short. I've already confessed I know nothing about this sort of thing, and I would appreciate your advice. Also, I did think I might be doing you a favour by choosing the drawing *you* liked best.'

Charlie took a deep breath and walked over to stand beside him. She pointed to her favourite.

'This one, then.'

Calum Sutherland gave it a perfunctory glance and nodded.

'Right, then. That's settled.'

His relief was obvious, and he went quickly back to his desk and pressed a switch on the intercom.

'Diary, please, Judy.' He turned back to Charlie. 'Half an hour, you said?'

'For the first sitting...'

'How many will you need?'

Charlie pursed her lips and thought rapidly. Better to be positive and alter the arrangements later than haver now.

'Three or four,' she hazarded, 'as a minimum. I can't tell exactly, since every subject presents different problems. You must see that,' she added on a note of desperation. She ran her hand through her hair as she always did when she was bothered, and her hazel eyes widened as she waited anxiously for his reaction.

He gave a grunt of what might have been termed unwilling assent, and turned to Judy Bannister who was hovering by the desk with his diary.

'When can I spare half an hour?' he enquired grudgingly.

'You can be doing other things at the same time,' Charlie reminded him brightly although not altogether truthfully, but at this stage she was prepared to say anything, just to get him to agree to model for her. Later, if there was to be a 'later', she could put him straight about what would really be involved.

'Out of the question,' Calum Sutherland snapped. 'Work like mine needs every ounce of concentration—I should have thought you'd have appreciated that, but perhaps the female mind works differently.'

Charlie rose swiftly to the bait.

'Not being a man, I wouldn't know, but it hasn't done me much harm—there were plenty of men in for the Trevelyan Prize, but it was me who won it.'

'I,' Calum Sutherland murmured as he took the diary from Judy, who was watching this rally with interest.

'I beg your pardon?'

'It should be "I", not "me",' Calum Sutherland pointed out. 'Obviously you were better at art at school than grammar.'

Charlie's mouth snapped shut as she glared back at him.

'I could fit you in next week—Tuesday—for half an hour, at the end of the afternoon. About four-thirty.'

Charlie nodded. 'I think I can manage that.' She tried to make it sound as though she were doing him a favour by rearranging a mountain of work, whereas this project was currently her whole preoccupation.

'Very good of you.'

Charlie flashed him a suspicious glance. Was he making fun of her? Surely not. There wasn't a flicker on that impassive, handsome face. She began to gather up the armful of drawings to replace in her portfolio, but was halted in her tracks by a hand placed peremptorily on her arm which set her nerves quivering as it communicated a vitality which ran through her veins with a thrill as unexpected as it was unwelcome.

She drew back as though she had been stung, but the gesture made no impression on Calum Sutherland who had his mind on something else.

'Just a minute, before you put them away. I'd like Judy to see them. She knows a bit more about these things than I do. Judy, if you had to choose one of these drawings of Miss Flynn's, as a basis for this portrait she's going to be doing, which one would it be?'

'To hang in the boardroom, sir, or in your flat?'

'Does it make a difference?' He swung round to face Charlie accusingly. 'You never asked me anything like that.'

Charlie accepted the challenge with equanimity.

'I didn't want to complicate matters—I imagined you'd select the one which you felt most fitted your image of yourself.'

Calum Sutherland raised his eyebrows with obvious suspicion as he considered her remark, but made no comment as he turned back to Judy. 'The boardroom, I imagine. If it's good enough . . .' He ignored Charlie's outraged intake of breath as he continued. 'As I told Miss Flynn, I have no desire to be immortalised, still less to see me staring down at myself every day of my life.'

He walked swiftly over to the window and stood staring out while Judy began her examination of Charlie's drawings of her boss. Charlie noticed that she gave them a great deal more attention than the subject himself had lavished on them. Finally the verdict came.

'That one . . . I think—yes, definitely.' She pointed to the study of Calum Sutherland's head and shoulders framed by the window. Charlie smiled delightedly.

'The same one we . . . Mr Sutherland . . . chose. That settles it, then—we're all agreed. I'll begin work on it as soon as I get home.'

Calum Sutherland sighed and looked pointedly at his watch.

'If that's all, then? I have a meeting in a few moments, haven't I, Judy?'

Judy nodded. 'I have the papers all ready,' she assured him.

'Right, then.' He glanced at Charlie busy putting the drawings away.

'As you clearly feel so much at home in my office you won't mind seeing yourself out, will you?' He paused in the doorway and looked sternly at each girl in turn. 'But I would stress the fact that it is not, definitely not, somewhere you can come and wander about in whenever you feel like it. It is supposed to be private,' he added forcefully, 'and I must insist you remember that.'

He swept a pile of documents off Judy's desk and strode quickly out of her office.

'Phew!' Charlie collapsed into a chair. 'I feel as though he's wrung me out and hung me up to dry. Is he always like that—how on earth do you stand working for him? Half an hour at a time is about as much as I can take. Goodness knows how we're going to put up with one another during the sittings.'

She stretched out her slim legs and sighed heavily. Judy perched on the edge of the desk with a wry smile.

'You get used to it. As long as you do what he wants when he wants it, efficiently and promptly, that seems to keep him happy.' She wrinkled her nose. 'No, happy's not the right word. I don't think he knows what "happy" means, not in the normal, human sense...' Her voice trailed away and both girls sat in a melancholy silence as they took in the implications of what Judy had just said.

'I suppose there's no chance of a cup of coffee—we could chat and you could tell me what makes your Mr Sutherland tick...without breaking any confidences, of course.'

'Of course.' Judy grinned, then shook her head regretfully. 'Sorry, Charlie, I've got a mountain of work to get through before he finishes that meeting he's just gone off to. Next time, maybe—I'd like that. We could have lunch together some time, too.'

All the way home on the train Charlie found herself, just as she had done after her previous visit to Sutherland Associates, going over each moment of her meeting with their chairman, though 'confrontation' would be a more accurate description.

Judy's words still echoed in her mind. 'I don't think he knows what "happy" means.'

What a dreadful thing to say about anybody, and how sad. But the saddest thing of all was that she simply couldn't feel sorry for him. The choice to drown all warm, human emotions in the tidal wave of ruthless ambition which had swept him to the very top had been his and his alone, as she told Annie later that day over yet another cup of tea at the old kitchen table.

'He's not very old, either...mid-thirties, I should guess, and I suppose he must have decided that ordinary, normal feelings—like kindness, consideration, and love too—were expendable.' What was it he had said when she'd asked about his wife?

'Marriage is a luxury time doesn't permit,' or some such phrase. She shook her head. Terrible to be so single-minded. She stabbed a crumb with a finger.

'He's certainly been successful...in both ways. Sure, he's got to the top of his chosen tree, but I've never met anyone so short on loving-kindness—or even plain politeness.'

Annie smiled sympathetically. 'Poor old Charlie. Your first big break and you have to land someone like that.' She sipped her tea thoughtfully. 'I'd quite like to meet him some time—you make him sound quite fascinating!'

'Fascinating, my foot!' Charlie pulled a face. 'A complete barbarian, that's what he is, with no more notion of what makes the civilised world go round than—oh, I don't know...' her restless fingers ran through her hair, disarranging the expensive cut she'd had for the prize-giving ceremony '...Attila the Hun. He'd prefer a framed balance sheet in his boardroom even to a Rembrandt.'

'Maybe you can educate him to the finer things in life?' Annie suggested innocently. 'Look on it as a challenge—poor man, you ought to feel sorry for him. Think of all he's missing.'

'He's past educating—it would be a waste of effort to try. That man's impervious to anything that isn't written in figures—and I don't mean the Miss World sort. In fact,' she went on thoughtfully, remembering something else, 'I think he actually despises women. We're useful for typing, making coffee and setting appointments, but that's about it.'

That wasn't strictly true, though, she reminded herself as she was preparing her canvas later that day. There had been that brief moment when he'd held her hand just a fraction longer than was absolutely necessary...but that was at their first meeting, or rather the first meeting after the encounter on the train. Today had been different. Today he'd seemed at pains to show no feelings at all other than those of aggression and combativeness.

Surely, though, deep down in the recesses of his nature, there must be some softer emotions she could tap—that was, if she cared to bother. Why should she, though, when he'd shown her nothing but antagonism?

Charlie set up the large drawing they had all selected as the one she should develop into the finished portrait and stared at it unblinkingly in a concentrated effort to penetrate the façade to the real man behind it. Her whole future career as a professional artist depended on what she made of this commission. It was very exciting as well as daunting, and she couldn't wait to begin.

CHAPTER THREE

By THE time Tuesday arrived, Charlie had made just about as much progress as was possible without Calum Sutherland in front of her. The general design of the portrait was taking shape, but that was as far as she dared go, however tempted she was to begin putting in more detail.

It wasn't until she began gathering up all the equipment she would need for the first sitting that something occurred to her which until then she hadn't really thought about except in passing. Where did she imagine the sittings would be held? Although she'd placed her model against an office background which included the view through the window, she couldn't expect him to allow her to spread all her paraphernalia round that immaculate room. And she was sure he wouldn't contemplate the inconvenience of travelling to Cambridge at regular intervals.

'What am I to do?' she wailed to Annie who stood watching in some amusement as Charlie trailed up and down stairs with all her gear before stowing it in her rusty old Ford Escort for the trip to London. 'How could I have been so stupid?' Charlie was clutching an assortment of bags containing all her materials which threatened to spill out all over the hall floor as she gazed helplessly at her friend. 'Calum Sutherland will be furious—again. He won't want all this cluttering up the place, and I can't say I blame him.'

'If he wants his portrait painted he'll have to put up with the consequences,' Annie commented.

'But he doesn't,' Charlie reminded her. 'It's the last thing he wants.' She gazed forlornly at the mounting pile of luggage. 'And this will put him off finally.'

Annie picked up Charlie's easel and went to open the front door. 'Come on, I'll give you a hand. I expect you'll find you've been worrying unnecessarily. There's bound to be a spare office they can find for your things, and the sittings too.'

But Judy Bannister's expression, when she saw Charlie's load of equipment, reflected all her misgivings.

'Not much more now.' Charlie tried to sound reassuring as she lugged her canvas into the secretaries' office. 'I'll set it up in Mr Sutherland's office and then I'll come and sit in here with you, if it's OK. I got the message loud and clear last time, and I don't want to risk incurring his wrath again.'

But what *was* he going to say when he saw his office, even with all her gear arranged as neatly as possible, and with dust sheets protecting the expensive carpet? She would have to work in here this time, but in future...what? She stared at the shadowy likeness of Calum Sutherland gazing at her from the easel as though he could provide a solution to the problem, but he gave her no answer. Maybe when he came...

Charlie glanced at her watch. Half an hour yet before the time set for her appointment. She wandered into Judy's office.

'Mind if I sit here?'

There was a chair in the corner, out of the other girls' way.

'Help yourself,' Judy smiled, 'but you'll forgive us if we press on, won't you? There never seems to be enough time to get everything done.'

To begin with, Charlie was quite glad of some moments to herself. She watched Judy and Sue hard at work, but her mind was full of her own problems, or, to be more accurate, the major one of what to do about finding a permanent base convenient to her and her sitter. Her mind tied itself up in knots trying to solve the insoluble, and she became increasingly edgy in her enforced idleness as she waited for Calum Sutherland to appear.

What was the time now? Half-past four. He should be here any minute.

To try to take her mind off her worries Charlie got out her sketch-pad and began to make drawings of Judy and Sue. Apart from this being second nature to her, as she had told Calum Sutherland on their first and unpropitious meeting, it did help to calm her nerves. This was going to be the first time he saw her in action, as a professional and taking charge of the situation, and it was vital to begin on the right foot. She must not dither and look unsure of herself or she would lose what little respect he might have for her.

'Can we see?'

'Oh!' Charlie gave a little jump at the sound of Judy's voice. 'Yes, of course—I was miles away. Here.'

Judy took the pad and went over to show it to Sue.

'You are clever!' Sue exclaimed. 'Look, she'd got you exactly.'

'And you,' Judy laughed. 'She's caught that earnest expression you wear when you're typing.' She glanced across at Charlie. 'I don't suppose we could have these— or are they important?'

'No—of course...take them.' Charlie checked her watch again. Another fifteen minutes had elapsed. Worriedly, while the other girls were admiring her sketches, she edged guiltily back into the chairman's office.

If he didn't come soon it wouldn't be any use starting—the light was already changing and soon it would have gone altogether, and she needed bright daylight for the effect she wanted. She flicked the spotlights on—no, they were too harsh.

Charlie's fingers ploughed anxiously through her hair, making it stand up in short, dark spikes.

'You look like——' Judy bit off the jokey remark she had been about to make about Charlie's punk appearance. 'What's the matter?'

'The light,' Charlie wailed. 'If he doesn't come soon, the whole afternoon will be a wash-out. I might just as well have stayed at home...and after all the trouble I've taken. I suppose you can't ring, hurry him up?'

Judy looked shocked at the very idea.

'No, of course you can't. Silly of me. But time's just as precious for other people as it is for him. I'll have to make him understand that.'

The chairman's secretaries made no reply, but their unspoken thoughts were clear enough. It would be a brave, even foolhardy person who took their boss to task on this or any other matter.

But by now Charlie's mood was changing from one of trepidation to impatience and finally seething rage. If he'd agreed to a definite time for her appointment, he should stick to it. If she'd been a business colleague he'd never treat her in this casual fashion. Just because she was involved in something outside his narrow world, and a girl...

She leapt up and prowled round his office again, gazing out of the window, but the view which had so enchanted her on her previous visit merely irritated her now. All those busy people down there—and here was she, prevented from getting on with her own work by the uncaring indifference of one man.

There wasn't even any point in putting out her colours on her palette; she might just as well begin packing everything away. Another twenty minutes had passed, and the whole day had been wasted with not a dab of paint added to the canvas. It was infuriating, and so was Calum Sutherland and, when he did finally deign to put in an appearance, she would tell him so.

She heard Judy speaking on the telephone in the other room.

'Yes, she is . . . right, I'll tell her. Five minutes——'

'At least he hasn't forgotten you,' Judy told Charlie, trying to pacify her as she paced about in frustration at the information that she would have to wait still longer for Calum Sutherland's arrival.

'Am I supposed to be grateful?' Charlie burst out. 'The whole thing's ridiculous. How can I work under these conditions? I may as well pack up now. He can whistle for his portrait.'

Angrily she marched back into the chairman's office and began sweeping up her tubes of paint and brushes into her bag and when, at last, she heard Judy's door open and Calum Sutherland's voice in the next office, she didn't even turn round.

'You're not going?'

Charlie deliberately continued stowing everything away without a word, though she was unable to prevent her breath coming faster as her senses registered the dominating power of his presence behind her. This time, though, she was determined to stand her ground and not be intimidated. Right was on her side.

When she was quite ready, and not before, she turned slowly to face him.

'My appointment was for four-thirty, Mr Sutherland, and it is now——' she glanced at the clock over the door '—precisely twenty minutes past five, and I'm afraid even if I were prepared to start work now, the light has gone. It would be useless even trying.'

'What do you mean, the light has gone?' The brown eyes flashed irritable sparks. 'It's not nearly dark outside, and there's nothing wrong with the lights in this building.'

He strode over to the wall and switched on a flood of artificial illumination. Charlie shook her head impatiently.

'I can't work in that... it's too harsh, not natural. I need the light from the window.'

'I can't see that it makes any difference... look, Miss Flynn, I left a very important meeting early to fit you in, and now you tell me you can't even begin. I'm starting to lose patience.'

Charlie drew in her breath sharply but, instead of making the angry retort that rushed to her lips, forced herself to back away from what could easily develop into an undesirable confrontation of opposing wills. Why couldn't he understand that she was a professional with a professional attitude and requirements at least as demanding as his own? She'd have to convince him somehow, or she could see that no more than the odd crumb of attention and time would come her way, quite insufficient for the concentration needed to produce a finished painting of distinction—and that was what she was determined to produce. Anything less would be no credit to either of them.

She wiped her hands on her overall—a new one in honour of the occasion—and walked slowly towards him, very conscious of his mounting irritation but resolved to have her say, once and for all.

'Could I explain something to you, Mr Sutherland? Perhaps you don't realise just what is involved in painting a large scale, finished picture—and there's no reason why you should, of course.'

Calum Sutherland spread his hands in a gesture of resignation. 'Go on, Miss Flynn. I'm here now. I may as well hear what you have to tell me.'

Charlie couldn't altogether repress a moment's admiration for the man. She could see why he had got where he had—once he'd committed himself to listen, even unwillingly, his attention was totally committed to the speaker. His sharply intent gaze held hers as he watched her marshal her words with care.

'You see, this is quite different from sketching. For one thing, on a purely practical level, it takes me quite a while to set everything up...and before you say anything,' Charlie went on hastily, forestalling any critical remarks concerning the clutter in the usually spotless office, 'I'll have to make other arrangements, but we can discuss that later——'

Calum Sutherland leant back against his desk and folded his arms.

'I can see this is going to take some time,' he murmured, more to himself than to Charlie.

She went faintly pink. 'I'm sorry, but I think it's best if I tell you exactly what's involved.' Her colour deepened as she recalled how she had deceived him to get her way. 'I know I said you could be getting on with work at the same time, and so you could for a while, but I wasn't being strictly accurate.

'It will be time-consuming, I can't disguise the fact, and I do need uninterrupted periods when I can really concentrate. It's no use your thinking we can fit in twenty minutes here, half an hour there, between meetings. I shall need you to myself for most of the time.'

Calum Sutherland's eyebrows rose lazily, and at last, amazingly, a genuine smile broke over his face. Charlie was simply too astonished by the transformation this made to the only too familiar severity of his features to repair the implications of her remark. If only he would smile more often! Somewhere, beneath that forbidding, uncompromising exterior, there was a real man with ordinary human reactions—she had begun to doubt it recently, but at last he had allowed them to surface.

Unaware of what she was doing, she let her eyes scan his face with renewed curiosity, considering each feature in turn—the humorous twist to the firm mouth, the faint laughter-lines beside the eyes now glinting ironically as they rested on her own face with equal interest.

'I'm taking a leaf out of your own book, Miss Flynn,' Calum Sutherland remarked lightly, noting her discomfiture with evident amusement. 'Two people can play that game, you know.'

Charlie quickly dropped her gaze to stare at the pattern on the carpet. His abrupt changes of mood were quite unnerving.

'I ought to explain...when I said I needed you to myself, I didn't mean...'

She wished now she hadn't started. Saying what she *hadn't* meant would make it sound all so much worse. She spread her hands helplessly and ground to a pathetic halt.

'If I didn't know you better, Miss Flynn, I might begin to wonder about your motives...'

Calum Sutherland stood up, towering over her as he took in her sudden confusion.

'But you don't know me, Mr Sutherland,' Charlie burst out in desperation. 'You don't know me at all, and that is what I was trying to explain earlier, but I don't seem to be able to make you see what I mean...'

Her voice trailed away. If only she hadn't embarked on this particular subject, and Calum Sutherland seemed totally disinclined to come to her aid. He made no reply, and when Charlie saw him look at his watch her heart fell. He was about to abandon her, and the portrait, yet again. She might just as well give up the idea of painting him here and now if she couldn't hold his attention for more than a few moments at a time.

He moved round to the other side of his desk and picked up his phone, his eyes fixed on Charlie's face.

'I'd like an outside line, please,' he said, and then, briefly:

'A table for two, Franco, please...at seven. Yes...Sutherland. *Grazie, arrivederci.* I don't know about you, Miss Flynn,' he went on, 'but I have had a long and tiring day, and if we are to develop a reasonably amicable relationship our discussions might be considerably more fruitful conducted in more relaxed surroundings.'

Charlie unexpectedly felt a sudden wave of fellow-feeling for Queen Victoria, who complained that Gladstone addressed her like a public meeting, but, like that redoubtable monarch, she kept her face straight as she waited for Calum Sutherland to continue.

'There is a quiet and rather good Italian restaurant not far from here, and if you have time before you need to go home I would be glad to offer you some supper—and that way you'll miss the rush hour, too.'

At the mention of food Charlie realised that she was actually very hungry, since she had had no time for more than a sandwich at lunchtime.

'Thanks,' she accepted gratefully. 'That would be very nice indeed.' And a bit alarming, she acknowledged privately, being alone with this man without the moral support of a building full of people and the chance of an occasional interruption to ease the moments of tension between them. But still, under the influence of food and wine, he might even mellow a little... She forced her attention back.

'I expect you can fill in the next hour or so,' Calum Sutherland was saying as he sat himself down at his desk and began sorting through a pile of documents. 'I have one or two matters to attend to, but you are welcome to remain here and do your worst.'

A brief flicker of a smile reached his eyes before he bent his head in deep and instant concentration on the business in hand.

Charlie moved as quietly as she could back to the easel and got out her paints again. She could at least work on the background and start on the basic skin tones of Calum Sutherland's face, check the shape of his head...

Soon she was as absorbed as he was, and it gave her quite a start when the object of her scrutiny briskly collected his papers together and swept them into his briefcase, snapping it shut and standing up, all in one swift movement.

'Are you ready, Miss Flynn?'

This time, Charlie couldn't help a laugh bubbling up.

'It's not as simple as that, Mr Sutherland! I have to pack all this up and put it in my car, which is in your underground car park. It'll take me a while.'

She could see him bite back the impatient comment which rose instinctively to his lips, and cut off the quick sigh. A small victory, but an important one, she congratulated herself as she deliberately finished the area she was working on before cleaning her brush and putting it away. Then she stood back from the easel to examine the canvas with a critical eye while Calum Sutherland was out of the office having a word with Judy. Did the girls always have to work so late? Charlie wondered, blurring a too definite line with a finger. What a demanding man he must be to work for, and how lucky she was to be her own boss—in spite of all the problems.

'One of the porters will help you down with all that,' Calum Sutherland told her as he came back into the office, 'and you can leave your car where it is. I'll drive you back here when we've eaten . . . if that's convenient,' he added almost as an afterthought. He was clearly so used to having his own way that considering other people's needs seemed to come only with a real effort of will.

Charlie covered her palette with clingfilm to keep the paints from drying out. 'That will be fine—thanks.' Out of the corner of her eye she could see him fidgeting with a pen, but made no concessions to his impatience as she took the canvas off the easel which she folded up and added to her pile of equipment.

'There,' she said at last, struggling out of her overall. 'That's all ready now—if I could just have a moment or two to tidy up?'

Charlie made herself as presentable as she could, thankful she hadn't come in the worst of her painting gear, although jeans and an old check shirt weren't exactly what she'd have chosen for a first date with Calum Sutherland—or any other man, for that matter.

First? She grinned at her reflection in the cloakroom mirror. What gave her the idea there would be others? They were mutually incompatible, there was no doubt about that, and 'dates' would certainly not figure in their decidedly prickly relationship, except maybe for purely business purposes.

She flicked back her short, dark hair and hastily dabbed on some lipstick, assuming that her host would appreciate a prompt dinner guest rather than an elegantly made-up one. After all, he had seen her workaday attire and presumably didn't mind that she wasn't dressed to kill—in fact, he had probably chosen the restaurant to suit her appearance as well as the occasion.

A big, cheerful man—Lewis, Calum Sutherland called him—helped her down with her gear, and stowed it away in her car. Her host had disappeared but there was the sound of a large, powerful engine starting up, then a large, powerful car glided up beside her old Ford. Calum Sutherland leant across and opened the passenger door.

Charlie felt her jeans and shirt outfit to be painfully incongruous as she climbed in beside him. This car demanded the most fashionable of evening attire to complement its sleek lines and luxurious fittings, but she said nothing and sat back to enjoy the short, smooth ride to the restaurant. It was hardly any distance at all, but Charlie suspected that the chairman of Sutherland Associates had long since lost the habit of walking anywhere—so much for her earlier, romantic vision of him striding over the hills—and also, judging from his rapt handling of the expensive car, driving itself was probably a kind of relaxation for him after the rigours of the day.

They glided to a halt in front of a small, unpretentious little restaurant a few blocks away, and Charlie wondered whether Calum Sutherland was such a regular customer that the proprietor—Franco, wasn't it?—kept a permanent parking space available for him. Living alone, as she knew he did, he'd want somewhere to have his solitary meals unless he were a keen cook, and somehow that image didn't seem to fit him at all. Lots of men did enjoy cooking, but Charlie couldn't see Calum Sutherland bending over a hot stove, pinny round his waist...

He couldn't see the grin on her face at the incongruousness of the picture she had conjured up, but she quickly rearranged her features as Franco bustled forward, greeting Calum Sutherland as the old and valued customer she had suspected he was, before showing them to a table by a window which surprisingly for London looked out into a courtyard at the back filled with tubs and pots that later in the year would be overflowing with brightly coloured flowers. As it was early in the evening only two other tables were occupied, and the atmosphere was restful and welcoming. Charlie could see why Calum Sutherland came here—no intrusive background music, pretty flowered tablecloths and yellow candles on the tables, and Franco's cheerful presence... She could feel herself unwind, and leant back in her chair to meet her host's face with a contented smile.

'This is a lovely place—so welcoming, somehow, and surprising right in the heart of the city. Do you come here a lot?'

Calum Sutherland took the menus from Franco and handed one to Charlie with an answering smile of appreciation.

'Quite often. It's convenient for me, between the office and my flat, and, as you have already observed, Franco manages to preserve it as an oasis of peace and calm in an increasingly frenetic world.'

The two men exchanged smiles of mutual understanding and Franco spread his hands in a typically Latin gesture.

'I do my best ... now, please, take your time, and let me know when you are ready to order.'

CHAPTER FOUR

CHARLIE settled down to study the menu, tantalised by the description of the dishes as much as by the smells coming from the kitchen. Calum Sutherland made no attempt to try to influence her choice but left her to make her own mind up, merely suggesting the wine they might drink with the meal, a favourite Chianti which Franco evidently reserved for his special customers.

He didn't seem inclined to talk, so they ate in silence for a while, but contrary to what Charlie might have expected it was not an uncomfortable silence, and, in any case, the dish of Parma ham and melon in front of her was worthy of anybody's complete attention.

'Mmm—that was quite, quite wonderful.' Charlie finished the last morsel and sat back with a sigh of regret. 'I don't know when, or if ever, I've eaten anything quite so perfect—it seems a shame to have to follow it with anything else.'

'But you're going to, nevertheless?'

'Afraid so,' Charlie admitted cheerfully. 'I couldn't resist Franco's description of something called *saltimbocca alla romana*—also, I'm still very hungry.'

She attacked a bread roll with gusto, raising a smile on her host's face.

'If you'll forgive me for saying so, you have a pretty hearty appetite for someone so——' He paused while his eyes scanned her slender figure.

Charlie came to his rescue. 'Someone so small, you were going to say?' She nodded. 'Yes, I know—terrible, isn't it?' She grinned at him across the table, heartened by yet another glimpse of the real man buried beneath the formidable exterior. She was beginning to think they might just be able to develop some sort of satisfactory working relationship, though she knew she would have to tread very carefully.

'Most women I know seem so anxious about their figures that they are incapable of enjoying a good dinner,' Calum Sutherland went on, unaware of the effect made by his innocent remark.

'Most women I know...' Of course he must know other women, lots of them, *and* take them out for expensive meals far more lavish than this... He might not have had time for marriage, but that didn't rule out affairs. He must have had several, an eligible, wealthy and successful man like him. So what was it to her? Charlie took another gulp of wine to try to quell the spasm of dismay in the pit of her stomach. Just because he'd made a personal remark, there was absolutely no reason to think he was interested in her in any way. She was nothing but a nuisance to him, and he'd only brought her here to discuss business. She looked up gloomily to find his eyes resting on her face, and coloured slightly. Was he a mind-reader as well as everything else? That sharp gaze seemed able to probe her very thoughts, but she was rescued from her uneasy speculation by the arrival of Franco bearing their main course, and, when they had both been served, Charlie thought maybe the time had come to broach the subject they were supposed to be discussing. At least that would put an end to her more fanciful imaginings.

'Do you think we should begin to talk about the arrangements for the sittings?' she asked tentatively.

'After all, that is why you kindly invited me here—to work out some system convenient to us both.'

She swirled some sauce on to a forkful of meat and waited for his response.

'Not only the arrangements,' he countered, 'but I seem to recall we were supposed to be getting to know one another better. What was it you said? "You don't know me at all," wasn't it?' He refilled their glasses, his enigmatic expression giving nothing away as he threw the ball back into her court.

Charlie suddenly felt very insignificant, and not merely physically. What was she doing here, having dinner with this powerful and important man, presuming on his time and patience—and why should he even wish to get to know her any better than he already did?

'Well?'

She forced herself to meet his eyes and cleared her throat nervously. 'I'm sorry,' she said, 'maybe I shouldn't have said that. Of course there's no reason why you should want to know me better...at all, that is...'

Her voice trailed away, floundering uncertainly, before she pulled herself together sharply. No, it didn't matter what sort of personal relationship developed between them, but the portrait did—very much.

She sat up straight and leant forward in her anxiety to impress him with the importance of what she was about to say.

'About the portrait, Mr Sutherland...'

To her surprise she saw him shake his head. 'No,' he said firmly.

'No?' Charlie quavered. 'But I thought you'd agreed——'

The auburn head moved impatiently. 'Not "no" to the portrait, but "no" to what you've just called me.'

Charlie opened her eyes wide in astonishment as it was his turn to lean forward.

'If we're going to get to know one another better—and there's nothing wrong with that so far as I can see—you'd better drop this "Mr Sutherland". Calum's the name—Charlotte.' He held up an imperious hand. 'And I know you call yourself "Charlie", but I couldn't. It's just not right for you. It's a man's name, and a nickname at that, and, if you don't mind my saying so, you don't look in the least like a man.'

Charlie was annoyed that after all these years she still hadn't outgrown the habit of blushing when her emotions were under pressure. She felt her cheeks grow warm now in the face of his appraisal.

'Quite impossible,' he repeated firmly. 'And what's wrong with "Charlotte", anyway? It's much prettier.'

Charlie was silent for a moment. This didn't seem the right time to explain, but Calum wasn't to be put off.

'Charlotte it is, then,' he averred. 'And now we've got that out of the way you can tell me about the portrait.'

He leant back in his chair and studied her quizzically.

'Tell you...?'

'About all it's going to involve. I'm here to be informed, remember.'

Again Charlie felt the impact of Calum's striking intelligence, which could bring his sole concentration to bear on whatever point someone was trying to make, so long as it was valid and interesting enough to hold his attention. She frowned as her fingers twisted into her hair, oblivious of the twitching mouth across the table from her. It was a long time since she'd had to try to explain and justify what her work meant to her, and not even her parents had found the art world so foreign as this man obviously did.

'You see,' she began slowly, 'to paint a portrait you need time for thinking, as well as for the practical part of actually putting paint on to canvas. I could do you a rough sketch...well, you know that...without spending a lot of time or effort on it. It would be a superficial likeness, quite convincing in its way, but to reach the character behind the face, and to try to express *that*— well, it does need uninterrupted periods of deep concentration. For both model and painter, I'm afraid. An hour here, thirty minutes there if I'm lucky and you're not called away to a meeting...that won't do.'

'It's a two-way process, then?'

Charlie nodded eagerly. 'That's just it. Even if you felt you had to be working you'd have to be *with* me, subconsciously, not resenting what I was doing, and then be willing to pose when I needed you to, and not just when you thought it was convenient.'

Calum deliberately forked up a mouthful of his chicken and eyed her speculatively.

'So where is this ordeal to take place?' he asked finally. 'With the best will in the world I don't think we can manage in my office.'

Again her hand strayed to her hair, her eyes wide and anxious. A smile flickered on Calum's lips but she barely noticed.

'I know—it was stupid of me,' she agreed. 'I can't think how I can have overlooked something so basic. How I can have imagined I could set up my studio in your office—or anybody's office—I just don't know.'

'So what are we to do?'

Charlie twirled her wine glass slowly in her fingers, keeping her gaze steady on his face. At least he wasn't showing signs of hostility—in fact, he gave every appearance of offering co-operation.

'Of course, ideally, I'd like you to come to my studio in Cambridge.'

'Cambridge...?'

'I thought you knew—I'm sure I must have mentioned it.'

Calum looked thoughtful. 'Yes, of course...the train.'

'Anyway,' Charlie hurried on, 'that's where my studio is, but it's no use to you, is it? I can hardly expect you to come out there every week.'

'Every week?' The dark brows shot up in consternation.

'Well, every two or three weeks,' Charlie conceded. 'It's up to you, but I thought you'd want to get it all over and done with in as short a time as possible. Still, you couldn't manage Cambridge, obviously, so I don't know what to do,' she ended helplessly.

Calum shifted his attention to his meal for a while, and Charlie decided to do the same—it was too good to let it go cold. She regarded him surreptitiously while his mind was elsewhere. It was dark outside, now, and Franco had lit the candles. The soft glow accentuated the bronze lights in the dark auburn head bent over the table and enhanced the shadows where the thick hair curled over his forehead, the lines etched from nose to chin. How she wished she had her pencil and paper!

'You're doing it again.' Calum looked up suddenly in accusation. Charlie blushed but grinned, holding her gaze.

'I know—shocking, isn't it? But I did warn you—faces are my trade, and you know that now, so I'm not going to apologise every time you catch me looking at you. I need to learn your face, in all sorts of moods.'

Calum leant back in his chair, steepling his fingers on the table in front of him.

'My mother brought me up in the belief that it is rude to stare,' he observed drily, 'but I dare say in your case there are extenuating circumstances.'

Her scrutiny couldn't be making him uncomfortable, surely, Charlie speculated—not a man in his position, always in the public eye. He must long since have got used to being stared at. Even so, she had to restrain a sudden urge to lean across and touch his arm in reassurance. She clasped her hands tightly together on her lap and smiled gently.

'I don't mean to be rude,' she assured him earnestly, 'and in time you won't even notice I'm staring. It is part of my job, just as you said.'

Calum's mouth curved in a wry smile. 'Yes,' came the murmured assent, 'I do see that.' He paused, then went on, 'As it happens, I have to go to Cambridge next week. I could at least come to your studio for one sitting, if that would suit you—and then we can try to sort something out for the future.'

'That would be marvellous.' Charlie's hazel eyes shone as a wave of relief swept over her. 'How long can you spare? An hour or two? I expect that would be enough—it's quite tiring sitting still for any length of time.'

'Now she tells me,' Calum groaned. He signalled to Franco. 'Coffee?'

Charlie nodded. 'Yes, please.'

'I'll have to let you know which day,' he went on. 'I'll get Judy to ring you and you can make the arrangements with her. But it will be soon, I promise.'

Charlie felt as though a great load had been lifted off her shoulders. At least one sitting was fixed, and at Calum Sutherland's own suggestion. Maybe he was warming to the idea after all.

She caught herself staring at him again, and turned her gaze quickly to the coffee Franco was pouring for her.

'You're going to drive back to Cambridge after this?'

'Yes—if the car makes it,' Charlie pronounced cheerfully, stirring sugar into her cup. 'I had thought I might spend some of my prize money on a new...a newer one,' she corrected herself, 'but I'd rather keep that intact for as long as possible, I think.'

She sipped the coffee appreciatively.

'Very wise, if I may say so. You might need to be in London eventually, for your work, and then the money would be useful for a deposit on a flat.'

'I'd thought of that, but we'll have to see how I make out. The deposit's one thing, but paying off the mortgage will depend on if I can earn enough.' Almost cheekily she grinned at him. 'And *that* will depend on you, Mr Sutherland.'

'Quite a responsibility,' he replied gravely.

'You do understand now, don't you,' she went on seriously, 'why this is all so important for me? I know it must be a great nuisance for you, and I'm sorry your uncle let you in for having your portrait painted, but I promise you I'll do my best not to bother you unnecessarily.'

'For goodness' sake, Charlotte!' Something almost amounting to exasperation sounded in Calum's voice. 'A contract is a contract, and I've already told you I always honour mine. You've explained your position, and your aims, very eloquently, and I accept both. Let's leave it at that, shall we?'

He pushed back his chair impatiently and Charlie watched him as he got up to settle the bill with Franco.

She could have wished for a more gracious consent to the project, but to get him to agree to sit for her at all was more than she could have hoped for at the beginning. Persuading him to relax and enjoy the experience would be her next and more challenging task.

Unobserved for once, she let her eyes travel slowly over the broad figure who now had his back to her, and something stirred deep inside her as she watched the strongly muscled body, the powerful shoulders thrusting beneath the smooth cloth of the beautifully tailored suit. She was, as he had remarked, so slight, and he so tall, that she had to tilt her head back when she wanted to look into his face. What would it be like to be held against that strong chest, enfolded in his arms... to feel the smoothness of his cheek against her own... against her lips?

He swung round to face her and again she sensed a moment's real panic that he could see into her mind and uncover the enjoyable fantasy in which her imagination was indulging. Her breath came faster as she crossed the room to where he was waiting for her, but her voice was steady as she bade goodnight to Franco. She followed Calum out to his car, and, just as she was waiting on the narrow pavement for him to unlock the door, a couple of young men pushed past, laughing and talking, forcing her to step quickly aside to avoid being knocked into.

She let out a gasp as a strong arm encircled her waist in a movement at once protective and masterful. Charlie scarcely had time to register the moment she had been romanticising about only minutes before.

'Hooligans!' Calum muttered, and turned Charlie gently to face him.

'Are you all right?' he enquired, showing no inclination to release her from his light yet determined grip on her arm.

'Yes—really, quite all right. They weren't looking where they were going, that's all.'

She felt the strong fingers tighten briefly, then, almost reluctantly, it seemed to Charlie, he turned to open the car door for her. She slipped in and fastened the seatbelt, her thoughts in a turmoil. It had all happened so quickly, but surely she couldn't have been mistaken...? Hadn't she felt more than mere chivalry in the pressure of his arm?

She glanced across at the strong profile silhouetted against the street lights, and again her heart gave a lurch. A real magnetism flowed from this man to which it was impossible not to respond...in one way or another. Time would tell how she would manage to deal with it, but she would have to try to come to terms with her emotions before their next meeting.

Calum drove back to the underground car park in silence, maybe—or probably, Charlie decided with a pang—already regretting the physical contact between them.

'So you'll let me know when you can come to Cambridge?' she asked prosaically when he'd slowed to a halt beside her old Escort. She laughed, and Calum turned to her in surprise.

'Sorry—it's just the contrast between my car and yours. Not exactly in the same league, are they?'

Charlie was no expert, but she did recognise class when she met it, and this car was a real thoroughbred. She had never travelled in anything remotely like the long, sleek creature which had purred its way along the city streets to Franco's and back.

She stroked the leather upholstery appreciatively. 'It's hardly been able to show its paces this evening, though.'

A boyish grin lit its owner's face.

'My one self-indulgence, this Jaguar,' he confessed, caressing the steering-wheel with an almost sensual gesture. 'My flat isn't very far away, and I could easily walk to work. Do me good, too, I dare say,' he added cheerfully, 'but to know I have this waiting for me at the beginning and end of each day still gives me a real thrill.'

He gazed out at the gleaming bodywork of the long bonnet and smiled, more to himself than to Charlie.

'When I was a lad all we had was an ancient van which broke down more often than it went. I vowed then that as soon as I could afford any car it would have to be a new one——' He broke off and stared into space while Charlie hugged to herself this first glimpse he'd allowed her beyond the public façade of his life. She waited, unwilling to break the thread of trust binding them so suddenly and unexpectedly here in these unlikely surroundings.

But there were to be no further revelations now, and Charlie decided not to try to probe further.

'It's been a lovely evening,' she told Calum as they both got out of his car, 'and it was a super meal. Thank you very much.'

She held out her hand, looking directly up at him. His face relaxed into a smile as he took her hand in his.

'It was a pleasure for me, too, Charlotte. I don't mind confessing now that this whole project has been quite a worry to me. I'm a very private man, and the prospect of being studied so closely and then represented on canvas for all the world to see has been, up till now, very distasteful...'

He paused, and Charlie took advantage of the hesitation to put in quickly, 'Up till now?'

Calum nodded, making no move to release her firmly imprisoned hand. 'You've managed to convince me that it won't be the alarming experience I was anticipating, and in fact,' he added, clearly surprising himself as much as Charlie, 'I think I might even come to enjoy it. We shall see.'

'In Cambridge.'

'In Cambridge,' he echoed, 'and after that...'

'After that, I just don't know. I wish you hadn't reminded me,' Charlie said helplessly.

'We'll come up with something,' Calum assured her. 'Every problem has its solution, if only you look hard enough.' He released her hand at last and shepherded her round to the driver's door of her car. 'By the way,' he said, as he watched her settle herself into her seat, 'do you keep all your work in your studio?'

Charlie was puzzled. 'Yes—why?'

'I'd like to see your paintings, if you don't mind showing them to me. I missed your winning entry, so I have no idea what sort of things you do—what I might look like when you've finished with me!'

'Fine,' she grinned. 'I'll have them ready...next week?'

'Next week,' he agreed, and stood back as she prepared to back out. Charlie put her head out of the window as she switched on the engine.

'This old thing isn't quite in the same league as yours,' she admitted ruefully. 'I think I could grow accustomed to luxury quite easily.'

'Who knows what you'll be driving when you're a rich and famous artist?' Calum rested his hand on the roof of her car for a brief moment. 'Drive carefully, now, and goodnight.'

It was a good thing there wasn't much traffic on the roads that night, for Charlie's mind certainly wasn't on her driving. All the way home to Cambridge she relived each moment of that surprising evening.

It had begun so unpromisingly, too, with being kept waiting all that time, then the light going before she could make any kind of progress on the portrait, and on top of it all having to cope with Calum's distinctly hostile attitude towards her and her work. What was it that had made him alter his frame of mind? Was it her attempt to convince him of her own professionalism, her plea for understanding...or was it some deeper, instinctive response to her as a woman that had finally won him over?

She slowed down to let a large, powerful car go past, and her heart skipped a beat as she recognised the make as being the same as Calum's.

It had been quite illuminating, that sudden confession in the car park, but surely his car couldn't be the only important thing in his life? What about people? He'd told her his busy schedule had no room for marriage. Did that go for other relationships too? What about those women he'd mentioned who couldn't enjoy a good meal for fear of spoiling their figures? That implied some sort of social life, though one which apparently gave him little pleasure.

What a strange man he was. He could be so hurtful one minute, dismissing her work and herself too as though they were of little or no importance to him, and then, without warning, he could be almost tender—protective, certainly—as he had seemed when he'd held her to him, or imprisoned her hand in his.

Charlie sighed. It wouldn't do to read too much into his uncharacteristic behaviour. He couldn't really care anything for her, and no doubt it merely reinforced his sense of power to feel her small hand locked into his. It was his way of dominating someone who was part of a world he did not understand or feel comfortable in— not as yet, anyway. It was up to her to remedy that, and at least he had promised to come to her studio, which was more than she could possibly have hoped for. It was a start.

CHAPTER FIVE

HOWEVER hard she tried, Charlie couldn't settle to any serious work during the time she waited for Judy Bannister's call.

'There's no need to bite my head off,' Annie remonstrated as she tried to pass the time of day with Charlie when they met one afternoon in the hall. 'You've been in a very funny mood, now I come to think of it, ever since you came back from the meeting with your Mr Sutherland.'

'He's not *my* Mr Sutherland,' Charlie snapped, 'and——'

'—and it's nothing to do with me,' Annie finished for her. 'I know, I'm sorry.'

She turned to go back into the living-room, but Charlie hurried after her, contrite and ashamed.

'No, *I'm* sorry, Annie. It's just that it all seems so disorganised, not knowing when he's coming, and everything. I want to start work in earnest. It's got to be a success.'

Charlie's eyes flashed determination, and Annie bit back the teasing comment she had been about to make. Her private thoughts about the effect Calum Sutherland was having on Charlie's nerves had better remain private, for the moment at least.

'If only he'd tell me when he's coming,' Charlie moaned for the hundredth time, 'then at least I could get on with something else. It's the uncertainty that gets to me.'

As if on cue the telephone began to ring, the sudden noise making them both jump.

'May I?' Charlie almost ran to lift the receiver.

'Is that you, Judy? Yes, hi...it's me. What? Tomorrow?' Her voice rose, her wide eyes making panic signals in Annie's direction. 'He might have given me some warning...I can't be ready...'

She saw Annie making calming motions with her hands and common sense began to seep back. Of course she was ready, who was she trying to deceive? Judy was saying something about going to ask Mr Sutherland if he could change the date.

'It'd be difficult, though, he's already fixed the meeting in Cambridge——'

Charlie interrupted her.

'No, no, don't say anything. Tomorrow will be fine. This will be the first sitting, and I was just getting a bit uptight—don't worry.'

Judy murmured soothing noises at the other end of the phone and Charlie sighed.

'Thanks. Just send him off in the right frame of mind, that's all I ask. Oh—what time, by the way? Ten...that early? Yes, I see...I'll be ready. Bye, then.'

'Do I gather that the great man is honouring us with a visit tomorrow?' Annie asked with interest.

Charlie nodded abstractedly and Annie grinned as the paint-stained fingers strayed hairwards.

'You don't exactly look the part of the confident artist awaiting an eminent client.'

'That's because I'm not,' Charlie admitted. 'Oh, Annie, I'm terrified. Suppose I make a hash of it?'

Annie slipped a reassuring arm round the slim shoulders. 'Of course you won't. You're good, my girl, very good, and you can't go wrong with a model as...'

'Difficult, moody, uncooperative?' Charlie suggested, not quite fairly, but even Annie didn't know everything about the evening she had spent with Calum.

'Challenging, I was going to say—that red hair...an artist's dream, I'd have thought.'

Charlie nodded slowly.

'I know, and part of me's longing to get down to painting him, but the other part is simply scared stiff!'

'I bet he is too,' Annie said. 'He won't know what to expect—a bit like being on the psychiatrist's couch, and unnerving to a man in his position.'

Charlie flopped down on the bottom stair and hugged her knees. What was it Calum Sutherland had said? Something about the project being a considerable worry to him?

'Looks as though I'll have to learn to be a nanny, as well as a painter,' she said ruefully, 'and that wasn't covered in our course at college!'

'You'll cope,' Annie told her. 'You'll be in charge, don't forget. Just be sweet, kind and firm and you'll have him eating out of your hand.'

But Charlie found it almost impossible to share Annie's confidence. The picture of Calum Sutherland eating out of her—or anybody else's—hand was not one which sprang readily to mind, accustomed as he was to getting his own way in everything.

Charlie didn't sleep much that night, and she got up early to check and double-check on the arrangement of her studio and on her equipment.

'Brushes, turps, rags, paints...' she muttered as she went over it all again. Had she all the colours she would need? She laid them out in order—blues, yellows, browns, reds...white, of course. White? Where was it? She knew she'd had it only a moment ago...

'Blast!' she swore vehemently as she knocked the top off a tube of Prussian blue, a powerful colour which always seemed to spread everywhere once it escaped. She reached for something to wipe her fingers—there was the white, hiding under the pile of rags.

'Calm down!' she chided herself out loud. 'You're being ridiculous—you've painted people before, lots of them, and you've never got into this state. He's only a man, quite ordinary beneath all the trappings of success. Take it in your stride!'

She glanced at her watch. Still half an hour to go...she'd make another pot of coffee, and she could leave it on to keep hot in case Calum Sutherland would like a cup.

She had just filled the filter machine when she heard the telephone ring downstairs in the hall.

When I'm rich I'll have a telephone in every room—or one of those portable ones, Charlie told herself as she dashed down to answer it hoping the caller wouldn't ring off before she got there. She snatched the receiver up.

'Yes, Charlie Flynn here?'

'Oh, thank goodness. It's Judy here, Judy Bannister. Mr Sutherland's secretary.'

Charlie's heart plummeted. He wasn't coming after all.

'Is he with you yet?'

'No,' Charlie said, her spirits rising again. 'I'm not expecting him for another half-hour. He will be coming, then?'

'Oh, yes, of course. It's just that...could you give him a message?'

'Yes, sure.'

'Could you tell him the meeting he's expecting to go to this afternoon has been cancelled?'

'Fine, no trouble,' Charlie replied cheerily, thinking she might now be able to persuade him to stay for the whole day, but Judy was still talking.

'Charlie . . . I should warn you. Mr Sutherland doesn't like last-minute alterations to his schedule. He might . . . you know . . .'

'Blow his top?'

'Oh, I don't know . . .' Judy's feelings were clearly torn between loyalty to her boss and sympathy for Charlie. 'Let's just say he might not be very amenable—at first, anyway. Just for a while.'

'I've got the message,' Charlie told her gloomily. 'Sounds as if I'm going to have a really fun time.'

'It'll be OK,' Judy said, trying to sound convincing. 'I hope it all goes well.'

So do I, Charlie thought as she put down the receiver. It wasn't exactly the most auspicious start to the day, but there was nothing she could do about it except wait for the great man's arrival and break the news as gently as she could.

Her foot was just on the bottom stair when there was a ring at the door. Post, she supposed—some packet too big for the letterbox.

'Yes——?' she began, then stopped. 'Oh, goodness, I wasn't expecting . . .' Her voice trailed off as her eyes flicked from the man standing on the step to the big car parked outside.

'I'm sorry I'm early, Charlotte,' Calum said pleasantly, 'but the journey didn't take quite as long as I expected.'

Charlie stood aside to let him come in and smiled uncertainly up at him as she tried to assess his mood.

Annie had been wrong. Nervous he certainly wasn't, but the slight narrowing of his eyes as he gazed quickly about him, and the compression of his lips, denoted a certain impatience simmering beneath the veneer of politeness. The expansive mood of the other evening seemed definitely to have worn off, and she still had to break Judy's news to him.

Charlie shut the door and went over to where he was standing waiting for her to show him the way.

'I've just had a message from Judy,' she told him. 'She said to tell you this afternoon's meeting has had to be cancelled.' She looked up at him in apprehension as she waited for the explosion. 'Perhaps you'd like to go back to London?' she added tentatively. 'I'll quite understand if you want to change your plans.'

Calum tapped his foot on the tiled floor and frowned abstractedly before drawing in a quick breath of frustration. Then he shrugged resignedly.

'Damn nuisance, but it can't be helped, I suppose.' His eyes refocused unenthusiastically on Charlie's upturned face. 'Now that I'm here we may as well keep to our arrangements and get on with your portrait. I'll have to make a call first, though.'

'There's the phone——' Charlie pointed towards it, but Calum shook his head.

'No, I'll use mine. It's in my briefcase.'

Charlie had noticed he had brought the case in with him but hadn't given it much thought till now. Was he proposing to try to work during the sitting after all?

'Well, shall we make a start?'

'Yes, of course...my studio's upstairs. If you'd like to come up?'

Charlie allowed herself a little sigh as they climbed the stairs in silence. Their relationship seemed to have gone back to square one—it was so disheartening. No doubt he had long ago begun to regret those more intimate moments he'd shared with her…Charlie shook her head to rid it of those particular memories and turned to more practical matters.

'Would you like some coffee before we begin?' she asked politely. 'I guess you must have made an early start.'

Calum looked as though he was about to refuse, but thought better of it. He nodded. 'Thank you very much.'

While Charlie busied herself filling the cups he wandered round the studio, examining the unfamiliar surroundings with an almost unwilling curiosity.

He paused by the chair Charlie had prepared for him to sit in, an antique mahogany carver, large and comfortably shaped to fit the contours of the body. She'd picked it up in a market, as she had one or two other small pieces of furniture which were arranged at one end of the large room together with an old sofa bright with cushions, so that it could be used as a sitting-room as well as her studio.

He stopped by the easel, his only reaction a slight lift of the eyebrows as he took in the canvas resting there awaiting Charlie's attentions. He said nothing, then passed on to the collection of drawings pinned to a board. He looked at these without comment, too, before coming to rest finally by the window where he stared out at the jigsaw arrangement of back gardens down below.

Charlie took the tray over to where he was standing.

'It's nice here, isn't it?' he said surprisingly. 'And you've made the room very comfortable—not as intimidating as I imagined.'

Charlie laughed. 'What did you expect?' She handed him a cup of coffee. 'You have yours black, don't you? Or is that only after dinner?'

Calum took the proffered cup with something approaching a smile.

'You're very observant, Charlotte.' He sipped it appreciatively. 'I do always have it black—and, to go back to my earlier comment, "intimidating" perhaps wasn't the right word. I don't know what I expected—something disorganised and messy, I suppose. Bohemian's the word, isn't it?'

Charlie grinned, seeing in her mind's eye his bare and clutterless office.

'We don't all fit into the stereotyped picture of your average artist, you know. This is my living-room as well as my studio, you see, so I like to keep one end of it comfortable. And I've tidied it all up as far as I can in honour of this occasion.'

The atmosphere had definitely eased, Charlie thought, watching Calum leaning against the window-sill as he drank his coffee. Perhaps this would be a good time...?

'Would you like another cup, or shall we start...unless you want to make that phone call now?'

Calum drained his cup and put it on the tray. 'I won't have another cup, thanks, but I would like to telephone. It'll only take a few minutes.'

He began to tap in the number on the cordless phone he brought out of his case, and by the time Charlie had come back from taking the tray out to the kitchen he had finished his call and was staring out of the window again, deep in thought.

She reached for her overall. Usually she wore an old shirt to protect her clothes, but she'd bought a new one for her previous visit to his office. It had a large pocket in front and buttons down the back, and the material was still stiff and unyielding so that her nervous fingers had quite a struggle with the buttonholes.

She let out a little cry as she felt her fingers being moved aside by a pair of strong, warm hands which deftly finished the job at the back of her neck.

She spun round, completely taken aback by the unexpectedness of his action, and Calum dropped his hands quickly and stepped back, his lips tightening as a shadow passed momentarily across his features.

'I'm sorry,' he said shortly. 'I didn't mean to offend you.'

Charlie reached out as though to touch his arm, but withdrew her hand at the last moment, colouring with confusion. Why did he always take her so by surprise?

'No, you didn't...that is...'

They stared at one another without speaking, and Charlie tried to read something of what was going through his mind, and at the same time come to terms with the emotions seething in her own. She must not allow herself to respond to this man's undeniable attraction. Better to remember only his brusqueness and his earlier rudeness...she simply could not afford to become emotionally involved.

There was an added tension filling the space between them, but Charlie took a firm grip on herself and tried to dismiss it from her mind. The portrait was what mattered, and she must concentrate totally on that, and nothing and nobody else must be allowed to get in the way.

'Would you like to sit in the chair now, Calum?' she asked almost gruffly as she turned away to fiddle with some brushes. She heard him walk across the floor and looked round to see him resettle himself in the chair. She took up her own position by the easel and studied him intently before picking up a piece of chalk and going over to join him. She stood looking down at him, something that gave her an encouraging sensation of power.

She allowed herself a brief smile at his perplexed expression.

'I need this to mark the position of the chair, and your feet on the floor, to refer to later. I do allow you to get up and move around, you know. But first we have to get the pose right.'

She had to touch him, there was no getting away from it. To get him into the position she wanted made physical contact between them inescapable. Charlie had to summon up all the professionalism at her command to withstand the response of her senses to the feel of his body and his skin beneath her fingers, and she dared not look closely into his face, but went about her business with a brisk efficiency which helped bring her back to earth and the importance of the matter in hand.

'Are you comfortable like this?' she asked finally when she was satisfied with the pose. 'Say now, and we can do something about it?'

'Would it make any difference if I weren't?' he grunted stiffly.

Charlie laughed. 'You can relax, you know, and yes, of course it would. I'm not a complete tyrant.'

She went back to her easel and took up her palette. This was it—the real beginning. The light was right, the pose was right . . . she must get as much done as possible before he had to move.

She worked quickly for about ten minutes, blocking in the areas of light and shade, getting the shape of his head right...then a strange, high-pitched buzz made her jump as Calum sprang from the chair to pick up his phone which he'd left on the window-sill. He didn't even look at Charlie, let alone apologise—he might have been alone in his office for all the notice he took of her.

'Yes, Sutherland here.'

Even in her exasperation Charlie spared a sympathetic thought for the caller getting the sharp edge of Calum's tongue.

He turned his back on her, apparently oblivious of her presence and of where he was as he rattled off questions and instructions that meant nothing to Charlie, who boggled at the huge sums of money being discussed.

At last, the call finished, Calum replaced the instrument less than gently, remaining where he was with head bent in deep thought.

Charlie cleared her throat and he swung round, his dark eyes flashing irritation.

'What . . .?' For a moment he seemed almost shocked to find he had an audience, then he recovered himself quickly.

'I'm sorry, Charlotte, but it's an important time for the firm just now . . . there are a lot of details to settle.' He made an impatient gesture with his hand. 'I hope we won't be disturbed again.'

He settled himself into the chair again, placing his feet carefully against Charlie's chalk marks.

'Like this?' he queried.

Charlie frowned. Something wasn't quite right—the angle of his head had changed.

'Almost,' she smiled, biting back the irritation at having wasted so much time and at losing her concentration.

She walked over to him and made as though to move his head a little to one side, then hesitated, her fingers only inches away from his face, suddenly aware of the intimacy of her action. She bit her lip, annoyed to feel a flush creeping up her own cheeks as her hands froze by her sides.

'You didn't hesitate last time.'

'No...well...'

'Come on, girl, stop havering. I won't bite.'

His skin felt warm beneath her touch and she was close enough to sense its faint fragrance, masculine and exciting. She could not prevent her breath coming faster as she tilted his chin to the angle she wanted, then she stepped backwards as much to put distance between them as to check his position.

Calum said nothing, a habit of his, she was beginning to suspect, when he sensed her confusion. She knew he was watching her closely as she returned to her easel and took up her brushes and palette to resume work, and again her senses became alert to that disturbing electricity charging the air between them.

When at last she did look up she found he was still gazing at her, and he caught her eye with a nod of approval.

'You really do know what you're about, don't you?'

Charlie at once began to bridle, but Calum stopped her with a motion of his hand.

'I meant that as a compliment. I'm beginning to understand what this is all about now...' The hand moved again to embrace the studio, the easel—Charlie herself.

Charlie stared at him, dumbfounded, but, when she had found her voice and began to speak, Calum was already lost to her again in a world of his own, a world of figures and balance sheets, profits and power...

She sighed. Understanding—respect, even—were all very well, but they were no substitute for undivided attention. He must be *with* her while she was working or his face would set into those formidable lines of granite which drained all the vitality from his features.

She racked her brain for something to talk to him about, and bring him back to the here and now.

'You come from Scotland, Calum? With a name like yours, and your colouring...'

She left the sentence open-ended and was rewarded by seeing his face lighten.

'I am allowed to talk, then?'

Charlie grinned. 'You're not back at school, you know, and it's better if you talk, actually, as your face stays relaxed. You don't look quite so dour then.'

'Dour?' One eyebrow rose fractionally. 'I've never thought of myself as dour, I must say. And yes, I do come from Scotland—Perth, as a matter of fact.'

Charlie looked up quickly at the dry tone. Had she overstepped the mark? She'd only been trying to make light conversation. 'I'm sorry, I wasn't meaning to pry.'

Did he really resent her questioning him about his background? He had told her he was a very private man, she recalled, but they had to talk about *something*. There must be something she could mention that wouldn't make him take offence.

She sighed. He still wasn't really relaxed—she could see the stiffness in his shoulders from here... This assignment was turning out to be very hard work in more ways than one.

'Oh, no!'

There was that intrusive buzz again, and once more Calum leapt up to renew his contact with his own world.

This time Charlie deliberately tried to deafen her ears to his conversation, forcing deep lines of concentration between her eyes as she glued her attention to the canvas.

She couldn't work like this, and it wasn't fair of him to expect her to. Ten-minute snatches were absolutely useless.

How long had he been here—an hour? A whole hour and nothing to show for it. It had been a complete waste of time.

She laid down her brushes, wondering whether it might not be better to give up now and forget all about the Young Painters Exhibition. Were the rewards of success really worth all this aggravation?

She stared miserably out of the window. It was a lovely day out there, but the early spring sunshine was wasted on her.

A soft footstep close behind her made her swing round to find Calum's broad figure standing beside her. For the first time an expression of real concern softened his gaze as he looked down at her unhappy face.

'I am sorry, Charlotte.' He touched her lightly on the arm, making her nerves tingle in swift and unwelcome response. 'I can see how irritated you are at these interruptions, but I think that should be the last. Shall we get back to work again?'

Charlie's hand instinctively covered the spot where Calum's fingers had rested as she followed him across the room. Blast the man! One touch and all her resentment had evaporated. It was as an artist, not as a woman, that she must school herself to react to him, she told herself sternly. However attractive he was—and he was, very, there was no getting away from the fact—she must not let herself be won over by an easy smile and the casual touch of his fingers.

'You couldn't turn that thing off, I suppose?' She gestured towards the phone still sitting on the window-sill waiting to distract him whenever it felt like it.

Calum shook his head. 'Sorry, I'd rather not. We're engaged in some particularly delicate transactions just now, and I like to feel I'm in touch in case of an emergency.'

Charlie sighed and watched as he sat back in the chair.

'It does make life difficult,' she complained as mildly as she could, 'when I don't know how long it'll be before you leap up again. I haven't done anything worthwhile so far—you might just as well have gone back to London.'

Calum looked up sharply, his brown eyes glinting with irritation, but this time Charlie held her ground, trying to keep her breathing under control as she faced his formidable presence. She saw him open his mouth but forestalled him.

'I am sorry if I sound ungrateful. I know it's a great nuisance to you to be here at all, and maybe the whole thing was one big mistake. Perhaps we should forget it—after all, I do have the money,' she ended with bitter sarcasm.

This wasn't at all what she had meant to say, but her frustration and disappointment had taken over.

'Is that what you really want? Have you taken on more than you can cope with, Charlotte?'

Charlie stared at him. The words were spoken lightly enough but his expression was unfathomable. Was he challenging her to throw in the towel? If so, he'd chosen the wrong person, she thought, her temper rising. She had a *right*—she'd earned it—to paint this portrait, and paint it she would in spite of every obstacle put in her way.

'Of course I don't want to give up,' she retorted hotly. 'This is the most important thing I've ever tackled, and

I want to make a success of it more than anything in my whole life!'

A sudden gleam of approval flickered into life deep in Calum's eyes. 'That's better,' he nodded in satisfaction. 'I was getting worried you were going to take the easy way out. Though it wouldn't have been what I've come to expect from someone as determined and ambitious as you've led me to believe you to be.'

Charlie's jaw dropped. What a nerve this man had. 'I don't give up as easily as that. If I did, I wouldn't even have got this far. It's not exactly a bed of roses trying to become a professional artist, you know!'

'I'm beginning to realise that.' Calum considered her flushed face and watched thoughtfully as her hand ploughed through her hair, leaving streaks of paint behind like highlights.

'And I'm sorry. I haven't made your job any easier, have I?'

He reached and stabbed a button on the phone, then leant back with a wry smile. 'There, will that satisfy you? It's turned off now, and if the stock market crashes we'll know who to blame!'

'Thanks—very much.'

Charlie shot him a look of gratitude before rushing back to the easel. She must get on before he changed his mind. If only he'd always look like this, relaxed and with a humorous glint in his eye which made his whole face come alive. Quick, girl, get it down before it goes...

She worked furiously and made such good progress during the rest of the morning that it came as a shock to both of them when they heard the grandfather clock on the landing strike the half-hour. Twelve-thirty!

Charlie put her brushes down and stood back from the easel, then looked across at her model. Calum hadn't noticed that she had stopped work and looked almost comfortable as he sat with his auburn head resting against the chair back, his hands folded on his lap.

A bubble of joy lifted her spirits as she realised that the path ahead now seemed much clearer than ever seemed possible after their first almost stormy meetings. She was going to finish this portrait, and it was going to be good. She could feel it in her bones.

She began cleaning her brushes and the movement finally disturbed Calum's reverie.

'Would you like to get up?' she called across softly. 'I think we should call it a day now. I know how tiring it can be, sitting still for so long, especially when you're not used to it.'

Calum got up from his chair and stretched again, reminding Charlie once more how big and powerfully built he was, and strong, too. The shoulders she had touched were all muscle—no unnecessary flab there. How did he keep so fit? she wondered. All those business lunches...

'Do you want to see?' She gestured almost timidly towards the canvas before raising her arms to undo the buttons on her overall, unsure whether to be glad or sorry that he made no move to help her this time.

Calum moved his head in dissent. 'I'll wait till it's finished,' he told her decisively. 'I might say the wrong thing—expect too much too early... I don't know. Best not to interfere in matters I know nothing about.'

The bubble of joy now erupted into a happy smile. 'So you are going to let me finish it, then?'

'I thought I mentioned at one of our earlier meetings that I always honour a contract,' Calum reminded her. 'I'm not about to make an exception on this occasion.'

'Oh.'

The bubble burst, leaving her oddly deflated. Why should she think this assignment meant anything more to him than a mere business arrangement? At least he was going to see it through, and she should be satisfied—and grateful—for that much.

'It was very good of you to come today,' Charlie told him, watching him pack away his cordless phone in his case. 'I promise I'll work as quickly as I can to get the portrait finished, and not disrupt your timetable more than I can help.'

'We both have our jobs to do,' Calum remarked coolly, 'and I dare say we can come to some mutually satisfactory arrangement.'

He walked briskly over to the door, pausing just long enough to look round to check whether he had left anything behind.

Charlie's heart sank even further as she registered his apparent lack of interest as well as the fact that he had not suggested a time for another sitting.

'Will you be having lunch with your colleagues,' she asked politely, 'or would you like me to suggest somewhere, unless you are going back to London straight away?'

The change of subject clearly took Calum aback, and he stared blankly at her for a moment.

'I really hadn't given it any thought,' he said, then grinned. 'I remember, you're the girl with the hearty appetite, aren't you?'

The grin transformed his face and gave Charlie courage to make a suggestion that surprised her almost more than it did Calum.

'I could eat a horse,' she confessed cheerfully. 'Concentration always makes me hungry, and I could make you some lunch if you like—there's some home-made soup, and I've got some cheese.'

'I wouldn't like to put you to any trouble...'

'No trouble at all, if you don't mind no frills. I think there's even some of Don's beer—he's my landlord. Oh, it's very good,' she assured him hastily. 'He's famous for it. It's much nicer than most pub beer, too.'

The normally grave features relaxed slowly into a smile of pure delight, wiping years from his appearance.

'How could I refuse such an offer? Yes, please. I accept with pleasure.' He gave a wistful sigh. 'I don't know when I last tasted home-made soup... and home-brewed beer. What a feast!'

Charlie looked at him suspiciously, but he seemed to be quite serious. How sad that ordinary home cooking had become a treat for him.

'Come on, then,' she invited him. 'Let's see what I've got. You won't mind eating in the kitchen, will you?'

'The kitchen will be fine,' she heard him murmur behind her. 'Just fine.'

CHAPTER SIX

CHARLIE sat Calum down at the table with a glass of Don's home-brewed beer while she prepared the lunch. In her small kitchen his broad figure seemed to fill the space round him, and it wasn't just a question of his imposing physique but of the formidable power of his personality, the strength of will which had brought him from his native Scotland and carried him to the top of his chosen tree.

She directed a doubtful glance towards him which he was quick to intercept.

'Something wrong?' her guest enquired mildly. 'Can I help?'

'I don't suppose I could ask you to give the soup an occasional stir while I get the other things and lay the table?'

'Why not?'

He picked up his glass and brought it over to the stove, smiling at Charlie's uncertain expression.

'I have done this before,' he told her. 'Maybe not for a while, but my mother sometimes gets me to help when I go home—though more often than not she pushes me out of the way, saying I take up too much room!'

Charlie paused, her hands full of cutlery.

'I wouldn't be so presumptuous,' she said demurely, 'but you are, well . . . imposing.'

Calum laughed. 'Imposing—I like that! It's not what my family call it.' He swirled the soup round in the pan, then put a finger in to taste it.

'Lovely,' he said appreciatively. 'An excellent cook as well as a successful artist—you're a very talented person, Charlotte.'

He licked his finger again with relish and Charlie felt once more that little flutter somewhere in the region of her heart as she watched the auburn head bend again over her saucepan. Swiftly she refocused her concentration on the meal she was supposed to be preparing.

'There must be quite a few things you have to give up on your way to the top,' she said thoughtfully. 'I don't know whether I'd like that. I——'

'I think you've got your tenses wrong there.'

Charlie looked up at him, puzzled. 'Tenses? I don't understand.'

'You should have said, "I don't know whether I *shall* like that." You *are* on the way to the top, or so you've always implied. In fact...' The large hand stopped stirring as he let his eyes stray over the girl now turned away from him as she cut some bread to toast. 'In fact,' he repeated, 'it was your single-minded ambition and determination that made me decide to submit to your desire to paint me. Against my better judgement, I may say.'

He looked at her quizzically, and Charlie went pink, unsure whether she should feel flattered or not. His very complex character never got any easier to fathom out.

An enquiry about the kind of cheese he'd prefer changed the subject less than adroitly, but Calum made no comment as he took his place at the table to allow Charlie room to pour out the soup.

Conversation was easier than it had been at Franco's, and Charlie even managed to forget that her guest was the eminent, formidable merchant banker who had so intimidated her on their earlier encounters. He gave every indication that he was enjoying himself as she watched him tuck into the very ordinary fare she offered him.

'That was quite delicious,' he said at last, stretching back into his chair with a satisfied expression. 'I congratulate you on your excellent soup, and your landlord on his beer, too.' He uttered a sigh of pure contentment. 'Quite the nicest meal I've had for ages.'

But he could never sit still for long.

'I've been thinking,' he said, leaning his arm on the table to fix Charlie with the old piercing gaze. She met his eyes with a mixture of alarm and expectancy—what was coming now?

'This painting business...' he went on, then hesitated. 'There's an art gallery in Cambridge, isn't there?'

'The Fitzwilliam, yes. Why?'

'Supposing we pay it a visit—you must know it well, living here? Show me your favourite pictures, give me a guided tour. Explain them to me. I don't know enough about your world—there's never a lot of time...'

'I'd love to,' Charlie agreed enthusiastically. 'When would you like to go?'

'This afternoon,' came the prompt reply as Calum got to his feet.

'Don't you have to go back to London?' Charlie asked, amazed at the abrupt turnabout of events.

'No one's expecting me, now the meeting's been cancelled, and it's one of the advantages of being boss that I can take time off if I want to.' He pulled Charlie's chair out impatiently. 'Come on, let's be off!'

'You don't let the grass grow under your feet, do you?' Charlie stood up slowly and began to clear the dishes. Calum grabbed a load of cutlery and dropped it into the sink.

'No. Once I make a decision I act on it immediately—and I expect others to follow suit.'

'I see. Well—you finish that, and I'll go and change. That way we won't waste any more time than absolutely necessary.'

Charlie grinned cheekily at him and was closing her bedroom door before he had time to turn round.

That'll teach him, she thought, half amused, half annoyed by the possessive way in which he'd commandeered her services and her time. She was annoyed with herself too, for so meekly giving in but then he always managed to get his way, didn't he?

She had no intention of hurrying, though. Calum might have bulldozed her into spending the afternoon with him, but she was not going to give him the satisfaction of seeing her rush to do his bidding.

She, Charlotte Flynn, was a professional woman in her own right. If she chose to give up her time to show him the delights of Cambridge, it would be on her terms.

Quite deliberately she took longer than she needed to change out of her paint-spotted jeans and shirt into a more respectable skirt and sweater, and by the time she sauntered casually down to the hall to rejoin Calum his old restlessness was beginning to make itself felt. She watched mischievously from beneath lowered lids as impatience and politeness battled it out for supremacy.

'I suppose there'll be somewhere to park?' He jangled his car keys in his hand.

'In Cambridge, in the middle of the afternoon? You must be joking!'

'Then how...?'

Charlie picked up her bag and went to open the front door. 'We can leave the car where Annie teaches.

There'rc usually a couple of empty spaces there, then we can walk from there. It's not far.'

As she climbed into the passenger seat of Calum's large car and felt it glide away, Charlie couldn't repress a pang of regret that they weren't going on a longer drive, into the country maybe. But that was a dream most unlikely to be fulfilled. It was extraordinary enough that she should be about to spend the afternoon showing him round the Fitzwilliam.

'Now, what exactly do you want to see?' she asked him when they were walking into the museum's darkly ornate entrance hall. 'There's something of everything here—Greek, Roman, Egyptian…English china, clocks, manuscripts——'

'And paintings?' Calum enquired. 'Portraits?'

'Quite a few,' Charlie acknowledged.

'Then show me some portraits,' he ordered her. 'I'm more likely to know where I am with those.'

He was as single-minded in his search for artistic enlightenment as he was in everything else, Charlie observed with amusement. The main staircase was roped off that day, and they had to walk through the lower galleries to get to the other stairs. Charlie usually darted from one case of delights to another like a bee after nectar, but Calum strode determinedly on in search of his prey. Portraits he wanted to see, and portraits only. He wasn't going to be side-tracked by anything else.

Charlie trotted after him, trying to match his long strides, but it wasn't till they had reached the first of the picture galleries that she finally caught up with him.

He stood in the middle of the polished floor while he waited for guidance, mentally dismissing some of the museum's finest Italian pictures, much to Charlie's chagrin. They were not what he had come to see.

Before she could say anything his eyes lighted on a portrait of two small boys, and he strode off to stand before it, transfixed by the study of the two grave little figures dressed in stiff, formal clothes and staring out at the world with big, dark eyes.

'Poor little chaps,' he murmured more to himself than to her. 'They look so anxious—told to be on their best behaviour and all dressed up like that. They should have been outside, running about in the fresh air——'

Charlie burst out laughing. 'You're supposed to be looking at it as a work of art, not worrying about the boys' welfare.'

Calum looked severely down at her.

'If—who is it, Titian?—can make me see those boys as human beings, worried, serious, anxious to do the right thing, then that's good enough for me.'

Charlie wandered on to the next group of paintings. 'What do you make of him, then?' she asked.

Calum followed her to where she was gazing up at a portrait of a cardinal whose eyes were looking sideways beyond the confines of the frame.

'Seems to be looking for a way of escape,' he said irreverently. 'And I know just how he felt.'

'You're not taking this seriously,' Charlie chided him. 'How can I explain why I feel the way I do about them if you're going to treat all these great works so flippantly?'

But Calum wasn't listening. His attention had been caught by the picture hanging next to it.

'Now this,' he stated firmly, 'this I can relate to. In fact I could put that on my wall with no trouble at all. I really like that.'

Charlie was surprised to discover that he was looking at a landscape.

'Just look at the light on the water, and on the hills behind.' He turned to her in delight. 'Now I'm beginning to see...it looks just my favourite loch back home. At certain times the light's just like that. Enough to make your heart dance, as my grandmother used to describe it.'

Charlie looked up at him in surprise, but he seemed so absorbed by the painting that she said nothing, glad that he'd found something to capture his imagination, which was, after all, what art was all about, so far as she was concerned at least.

She left him there and went off in search of one of her own favourite portraits, a small Rubens high up on the wall. It was her turn to lose herself in contemplation, and she didn't hear Calum's silent approach, nor see the gleam in the watchful brown eyes as he stood close behind her, a half-smile playing on his lips.

'Penny for them?' he said at last.

Charlie gave a little jump, and turned at the sound of his voice. She smiled. 'If only I could do something a quarter as good as that, I'd die happy.'

Calum looked from Charlie to the painting and back again. 'Why?' he asked in curiosity.

'Look at the mocking light in those eyes—world-weary, cynical. Rubens has caught the real individuality of his character...what all portrait painters hope to do.'

'Is that what you're aiming to do to me? Search out my hidden depths and expose them for all to see?' Her pupil sounded alarmed.

'Of course,' Charlie said, with wide-eyed innocence. 'Didn't I explain that early on?'

Calum shook his head. 'You may have done. I don't think I took it all in. But now...' he nodded towards the painting Charlie had been talking about '...I'm beginning to understand just a little, though of course I shall need a lot more tuition before I can even begin to grasp what you're trying to achieve. A lot more,' he added in a low voice.

He took a step nearer until their bodies were as close as they could be without making contact. Charlie sensed her instincts stir into a response as she felt—knew—he wanted to touch her. She dropped her eyes and her pulses began to quicken. But did she want him to?

Now was the time—now, before it was too late to turn back—to make the decisive movement that would tell him more clearly than any words that she didn't want to go down that path, but her body refused to obey the feeble impulse from her brain and she remained rooted to the spot.

Her breath came faster and she dared not move nor look up for fear of betraying her emotions. Calum kept quite still, a hair's breadth away, but the magnetism emanating from his proximity was all the more powerful for being so controlled.

'I think we've seen enough for one day.' Charlie could hear an unevenness in her voice, which sounded several tones higher than normal, and her feet still refused to move her away from the danger spot as she remained hypnotised by the man at her side. She forced a laugh. 'We don't want you to get cultural indigestion!'

'You haven't answered my question.' He spoke softly from somewhere above her head, with no hint of his customary abrasiveness.

'I didn't know it was a question. It sounded to me more like a statement...or even a command.'

She heard him draw in his breath sharply and the movement, slight though it was, rocked him towards her so that she felt his jacket brush against her arm.

'I'm sorry.'

It was the note of compunction that finally made her turn, slowly, to look at him, and as their eyes met he spread his hands in a gesture of apology.

'It wasn't meant to sound like that, not at all. I've really enjoyed this afternoon, and I'm very grateful to you for giving up your time...truly.'

He sounded so unlike his usual autocratic self that Charlie had to fight hard against her instinct to reach out to reassure him.

'I would be even more grateful if we could repeat the occasion. What about the National Gallery next time?'

Charlie took the opportunity to slip sideways through the gap between Calum's broad figure and the wall, putting a safer distance between them. The danger had receded...for the moment.

She smiled uncertainly up at him. 'I've enjoyed myself too, and of course I'll go with you round any museum or gallery you like. In fact, it'll be hard to stop me— just think of them all...you'll be sorry you started.'

'I doubt it.'

Their eyes locked and almost imperceptibly the auburn head bent towards her... A wave of mingled regret and relief swept over Charlie as a tinkling clock broke the spell.

'Three o'clock already!' she exclaimed with false brightness. 'What time do you have to leave Cambridge?'

'I'd hoped——' Calum began, then stopped. The moment had passed. 'I'd not really thought,' he said, 'but it doesn't matter when I go back.'

'In that case,' Charlie said, 'there's something else I'd like to show you, unless you've been there before. King's College Chapel?'

Calum shook his head. 'I've never had the time.'

'You can always make time for the really worthwhile things in life,' she lectured him severely. 'How often do you come to Cambridge for meetings?'

'About once a month, I suppose.'

'That's disgraceful, coming here so often and never once taking the trouble to see one of the glories of England—of the whole world, I should say.'

They walked along the road from the museum in easy companionship, the earlier tensions evaporating in the warm spring sunshine.

'I suppose everywhere looks at its best at this time of year,' Charlie remarked. 'The trees and grass are all so fresh—look there...' She pointed through some railings at one of the college gardens. 'All the greens are so bright, yet subtly different from one another. A painter's paradise—and nightmare!'

Calum laughed with her, then shook his head in rueful admiration. 'You're showing me things I'd never noticed before. I'd always assumed all greens were much the same—except for conifers, I suppose. Dark or light—but just green!'

'Oh, dear,' Charlie sighed in mock despair. 'What a lot you have to learn—but we'd better keep that lesson for another time. I'm not sure whether they'll be closing the chapel for evensong, so we ought to hurry.'

Calum followed her obediently as she wove her way through the crowd of students and tourists streaming along the path skirting the great lawns to the entrance to King's College Chapel. She paused outside, her eyes shining.

'I wish I were seeing it for the first time. I do hope...oh, come on!'

She caught his arm in her eagerness to share her delight with him and guided him into the chapel. 'No matter how often I come here, I still get shivers down the spine,' she whispered.

She was about to say something else, but the expression on his face told her to be silent, and to allow him to drink in the marvels of the place without interruption from her.

Gently she removed her hand from his arm, but he seemed oblivious to everything as he stood, dwarfed for once by the magnificence of the building and gazing round in stunned admiration.

At last his eyes came back to her.

'I'd never have believed it,' he breathed, 'never. Those pillars—they're like something growing, the way they spread out like branches.'

'Fan-vaulting,' Charlie told him prosaically, then wished she hadn't.

Calum brushed aside the definition with an impatient hand. 'It doesn't matter what it's called. It's a miracle.' He shook his head, bright copper in the sun filtering in through the stained glass. 'And the light... Most cathedrals I've been to have been dark, gloomy places— but here...it's amazing, isn't it, what man can achieve?'

His head tilted back to stare at the delicate stone tracery swirling way above him, then, after a while, and looking rather dazed, he straightened up and turned back to her.

'I am very grateful to you, Charlotte, for bringing me here, and I'm not sure it wasn't worth waiting for. My horizons have definitely been expanded this afternoon, and I have only you to thank for it.' A smile of pure pleasure lit his face. 'One ought to have some surprises left for middle age.'

'Middle age!' Charlie burst out loudly enough to amuse some nearby tourists. She dropped her voice to a whisper. 'You're not middle-aged!'

'Compared to you, I should have thought I must seem very middle-aged.' His eyes, glinting with amusement, ran appraisingly over her, coming to rest on her heart-shaped face beneath its cap of dark hair. 'How old are you—twenty-two, three?'

'It's not done to ask a lady her age,' Charlie retorted stiffly. 'Twenty-four, actually. Almost a quarter of a century.'

'Well, I confess to being thirty-eight...definitely middle-aged compared with someone a mere twenty-four.'

'You're as old as you feel,' Charlie replied tritely, 'and age is only relative. The men who built this chapel wouldn't have expected to live much beyond the age of thirty-five.'

Calum still looked rather dazed as they emerged some time later into the sunshine.

'Any other revelations?'

Charlie smiled. 'I think that's enough for one day. We don't want to overdo it, and I've taken up quite enough of your time...a whole day, almost.'

'Terrible, isn't it?' The dark eyes shone with almost boyish glee. 'And it's far too late to do any work now, and the light will be going soon, won't it, so you can't do any more painting? You see, I do remember what you tell me, Charlotte. Tell me something else,' he went on as they walked slowly out into the street. 'Why didn't you want me to call you Charlotte?'

Charlie was silent for a moment. 'That's what my parents call me,' she replied flatly. She walked on ahead of him.

Calum lengthened his stride to catch up with her.

'Do you not get on with your parents?' he asked quietly, then added quickly, 'I'm sorry, I had no right to ask. It's none of my business.'

Charlie shook her head and stopped to stare with unseeing eyes into the nearest shop window.

'No, it's all right. It's not very interesting or dramatic.' She shrugged. 'It's simply that my mother and father— well, Mother mostly—never wanted me to be an artist in the first place.'

'Any particular reason?'

'Mother has what you might call social pretensions. She couldn't bear the thought of anyone in the family mixing with what she always calls "those dreadful Bohemians".' Charlie laughed. 'She had—still has, I expect—the most weird ideas of what painters get up to. Drugs and immoral practices of all kinds... you can imagine. And all that nude modelling! When I was at college she made me hide away all my life drawings and paintings for fear anyone might set eyes on them and become corrupted by the sight of the naked human body! By "anyone" she meant her bridge and golfing chums. She's a dreadful snob!'

'What would she have liked you to be?'

Charlie shrugged and began to walk on slowly. 'Almost anything else. My sister's a cordon bleu cook and is thinking of setting up her own business.'

'And that's respectable?'

'Very. You see,' she went on in a lighter tone, 'Ma's one aim is to see us both successfully married off, and she thinks Sara—my sister—is likely to meet a whole range of eligible bachelors at one of the posh parties she caters for.'

'And you won't?'

There was a real lilt of amusement in the deep voice, and Charlie lifted her eyes to his, opening them wide in mock innocence.

'Of course not. The art world is full of shady characters, either drug-pushers or left-wing anarchists . . . no one I could marry!'

'And what about your respectable, affluent clients who are going to pay you exorbitant sums of money to have their likenesses perpetuated on canvas? Surely they might come up to your mother's expectations?'

The words were spoken lightly enough, but there was an undoubted gleam in the dark eyes that rested on Charlie's upturned face, and she turned away swiftly for fear of what he might read there. This line of questioning was close to dangerous territory as her quickening pulses warned her.

'I don't think she's thought that far ahead.'

There was a pause. 'And you, Charlotte—have you thought that far ahead? Or has one of those terrible Bohemians already captured your heart?'

The heart in question lurched painfully, but she steeled herself to match the lightness in his tone.

'To quote something you once said, Mr Sutherland, marriage is a luxury my schedule can't afford.'

She hoped she hadn't gone too far, but he wasn't to know she'd said almost the first thing that had come into her head—anything to prevent images of David, her 'terrible Bohemian' as Calum had described him with unwitting accuracy, from blotting out everything else. She'd had to struggle so hard to forget him, and had thought she'd succeeded. Did it still only need a casual remark to bring back the pain of their parting?

But Calum hadn't appeared to notice anything amiss. If anything he seemed to be amused by the spirited retort which adroitly side-stepped his question.

'*Touché*, Miss Flynn—very neat!' His mouth twitched gently, but the smile faded as he looked down at the bent head beside him and a silence fell between them before he went on almost casually, 'To change the subject, we haven't made any plans for another sitting, have we? I was wondering, would it make things easier if I came to your studio again?'

'Oh, would you? That would be marvellous!' The words burst out eagerly. Charlie had quite deliberately put all her worries about future arrangements from her mind so as to be able to direct all her concentration on her painting, and since lunchtime events had taken such an unexpected direction they had been forgotten altogether; until now.

'Also,' Calum went on, 'I should like to return your hospitality. Lunch will be on me next time—if you'll let me.'

'That would be lovely,' Charlie accepted with a lift of the spirits that had very little to do with the prospect of being able to continue the portrait in her own studio. 'How soon could you come?'

Calum pulled out his diary and perused it, frowning. 'Let's see... what about a week today?'

A sense of disappointment swept over her as she nodded agreement, but she could hardly have reasonably expected him to come again any sooner.

'That'll be fine. I'll look forward to it.'

'So shall I, Charlotte.' He reached for her unprotesting hand and held it prisoner in his own warm grasp. 'Thank you for today,' he said softly. 'It's been so very... so enjoyable.'

Their eyes met and held in something disturbingly more than mere mutual understanding, and Charlie's heart pounded painfully in her chest as she felt the strong fingers tighten round her own.

This won't do, she kept telling herself. Keep your distance, girl, you mustn't get involved again...you learnt your lesson with Dave.

Even so, it was with a surprisingly sharp sense of loss that she watched Calum climb into his car a short time later and glide out of the car park to join the traffic and disappear from sight.

CHAPTER SEVEN

THE next seven days dragged by with exasperating slowness and it wasn't long before Charlie came to realise that it wasn't only from professional necessity that she found herself gazing so often at the shadowy outlines of Calum's likeness on her canvas, nor was it only an artistic response that flickered in the region of her heart as she recalled that dangerous moment in the museum and the warmth of his fingers when he'd said goodbye.

She *must* keep her emotions under strict control, though, she kept telling herself, however attractive and fascinating she was beginning to find him. She simply couldn't afford to become involved in any relationship that wasn't strictly businesslike and impartial.

Stay cool next time you see him, and remember Calum Sutherland is only your model. That's all.

Now, as she saw him standing on the front doorstep, his hand poised to ring for the third time, she forced herself to disregard the unwelcome lurch in her chest and stared at him frostily.

'You were expecting me, weren't you?' Calum asked Charlie accusingly. 'You were a long time coming.' He peered more closely at her as she stood in the doorway blocking his entrance. 'You look cross, Charlotte. Not with me, I hope?'

Of course she was cross, and why shouldn't she be? Who wouldn't be cross at being kept waiting for half a morning, and small wonder she had deliberately taken her time to answer his insistent ringing. Last time he had arrived soon after nine, and what time was it now? Almost eleven o'clock.

'Something came up,' Calum said, noting the irritable glance at her watch. 'Something rather important that I didn't want to put off.'

He smiled at her with no attempt at an apology.

'I realise that you must have more important calls on your time than your sittings here with me, but I do have a telephone,' Charlie retorted tartly. 'You might have let me know if you were going to be late. My work's important, too.' She stood aside to let him into the house. 'I did begin to wonder if you'd changed your mind about coming today.'

She marched over to the stairs without turning to see whether he were following, and heard his firm step behind her on the tiled floor of the hall. She wasn't going to be put off by a disarming smile—especially when he hadn't even apologised for being so late.

'You're a great one for quoting my remarks back at me, Miss Flynn. Perhaps it's slipped your mind, but I believe I tried to impress on you that I always honour my agreements.'

Charlie's heart sank as she cursed her quick tongue. 'Miss Flynn' again, was it? She shouldn't really have taken him to task so sharply—it must have sounded very impertinent. It was easy to forget the power and importance of his position when her own mind was so obsessed with the portrait.

Halfway up the stairs she turned to face him, and found herself looking disconcertedly deep into his eyes, now on a level with her own.

'I do remember,' she admitted with chagrin, as she ran her fingers through her hair. 'Especially disagreeable ones, you said. It was just that you came so early last time, so I expected...'

She let the sentence fade and didn't go on to tell him that her annoyance had in part stemmed from anxiety. He hadn't seen her pace the studio floor, checking the time, peering out of the window to catch the arrival of the large, sleek car.

Supposing he'd had an accident, she'd thought, staring down the obstinately empty road. He was probably driving too fast—most men did, especially in cars like that.

Charlie had felt quite sick at the memory of recent pictures she'd seen on TV of smashed cars and bodies in a motorway pile-up, before pulling herself up sharply.

'For goodness' sake, girl,' she'd scolded herself out loud. 'He'll have had some emergency at the office...' Then why hadn't he rung?

There was a flicker on the handsome face so close to hers, the lines of which were now so familiar to her. She caught the scent of him, masculine and disturbing, and she backed away up the stairs in retreat.

The flicker faded but he held her gaze. 'If I hadn't wanted to come, there are plenty of things to keep me in London. But I promised I'd be here, and I always keep my word, and I've taken another whole day off for you.'

'The whole day—this afternoon as well?' Charlie couldn't disguise her surprise.

They walked on slowly up the stairs, and Calum caught up with her on the landing.

'Certainly this afternoon as well. *You* hadn't forgotten, had you, that I'm taking you out to lunch?'

Charlie was taken aback at the note of real concern in his voice. 'No, of course not. I've been looking forward to it. Very much.' She paused, then smiled uncertainly up at him. 'But lunches don't usually take all afternoon.'

'Not normally,' he agreed, but didn't elaborate any further as he crossed the studio floor to the waiting chair.

Charlie let the subject drop, in spite of a burning curiosity to find out more, and knelt at his feet to check their position against the chalk-marks.

'That'll be two afternoons you'll have taken off. Don't you feel guilty?'

'Not in the least,' came the prompt reply. 'As a matter of fact, I think it could even become a habit—with the slightest encouragement.'

Remembering her earlier resolution, Charlie ignored the provocative remark as she stood up again to consider him, head on one side.

'I expect it's very good for you, taking time off now and again. I guess you don't do it very often, do you? When did you last have a holiday?'

The dark brows drew together in a puzzled frown as though the very word were foreign to him.

'Holiday...?' he repeated slowly. 'Do you know, I can't remember?'

'That's terrible!' Charlie burst out. 'Everyone needs a holiday of some sort—a break, even a short one. Do you mean to say you go to work every day of the year?'

Calum nodded. 'Except when the building's closed— Bank Holidays, Sundays...though sometimes...'

'Sometimes you work Sundays too?' Charlie sighed and looked at him in pity. 'No wonder you'd never been to King's College. Do you ever take time just to enjoy yourself?'

'I don't see——' Calum began irritably, then nodded briefly. 'As you're so concerned about my welfare, it might reassure you to know that I do play squash once or twice a week, and there's a gym round the corner from the office where I go for a work-out as regularly as I can, but working hard is no hardship for me, Charlotte. It's my life, and I enjoy it!'

The retort came sharply, another firm reminder of who he was, the importance of his status in his own world.

Charlie bit her lip and worked in silence for a while, but it was no good. The old, familiar lines had reappeared on his face, the set of his shoulders subtly altered by the change in his mood.

She put down her brush and palette and walked over to the chair to stand behind him with her hands resting on his shoulders.

'Relax,' she told him quietly. 'Your muscles are all taut—just forget your work for once, and please forget what I said just now, too.' She sighed. 'I'm sorry if I keep saying all the wrong things today. It's none of my business how you spend your time.'

She couldn't see the expression on his face, but gradually she sensed the tension ease away from him beneath her fingers and simultaneously the atmosphere between them lightened. For a while she remained where she was, secretly relishing the feel of the hard muscles under her hands, and again she felt her nerve-ends tingle at the intimacy of the physical contact.

She stared at the back of the auburn head, noting the small bronze curls brushing the back of his collar, the appealingly childlike curve of his ear, and at the same time something stirred deep within her. Her hands would only have to inch up to touch the smooth skin of his neck, so vulnerable below the aggressively springing hair...

Quickly she dropped her hands to her sides and retook her place at the easel, keeping her head bent to hide the new brightness in her eyes.

'Am I forgiven?' she asked lightly when she was safely out of his direct line of vision. 'You'll still take me out to lunch?'

At last a smile. Charlie set to work quickly.

'Hungry already?'

'You know me,' she countered. 'Your typical starving artist!'

The smile broadened. 'I remember—in fact...'

This was better, Charlie thought happily. If only she could keep him talking, all the lines would vanish, leaving only that light in his eyes that so transformed his whole face.

'Yes?' she encouraged him. 'In fact what?'

He shook his head gently. 'Nothing...it'll keep.'

Charlie managed to keep their conversation going in a light-hearted manner that she would never have thought possible after their first encounters. To have this combative, arrogant man actually here in her studio for a second time and apparently beginning to tolerate, if not actually enjoy, the experience he had so rudely dismissed as a waste of time was an achievement almost as great as winning the Prize itself!

She still had to tread carefully in case he took offence at some thoughtless remark, but at last some kind of understanding seemed to be growing between them, and she could actually begin to enjoy herself.

In spite of their late start, by the end of the morning the painting was really beginning to take shape. In fact, thought Charlie, usually her own severest critic, in some places there was little left to do. If she went on adding and altering she might very easily destroy that spark of real character she knew she had managed to capture.

She looked across at Calum as he unwound his limbs and stretched in evident relief.

'Would you like to see it?' she asked diffidently. She gestured towards the canvas, studying first her model then his likeness with a certain satisfaction. 'I hope...I think you'll be pleased with how it's coming on.'

But Calum shook his head decisively. 'I told you, I'll wait till it's finished,' he told firmly. 'If you don't mind,' he added as though remembering his manners.

Charlie tried to hide her disappointment, but he was the client—it was his wishes that counted.

'No, you must do what you feel is right.'

She busied herself cleaning her brushes and wiping away the spots of paint she always managed to collect on herself while Calum crossed to the window.

'It's still fine,' he remarked, and Charlie looked up at the evident satisfaction, almost relief, in his voice. It wasn't like him to bother about the weather. She saw him look anxiously up at the sky before turning back to face her. 'I think we should be off soon.'

No doubt he had booked a table somewhere and wanted to be sure of getting to the restaurant by the arranged time, in case they gave it to another customer. Maybe a restaurant with a garden...

'I'd better change and tidy myself a bit.' Charlie looked down ruefully at her old, stained clothes and trainers. 'I won't be long, though—I promise.' She paused in the doorway. 'I dare say it'd be impolite to ask where we're going—but could you give me some idea of what I should wear? You look very formal...'

'Heavens—I don't know! I'm no expert in women's fashions.'

'Formal or casual, then?'

'Casual,' Calum said firmly. 'Definitely casual.'

Still curious as to their destination, Charlie decided it must be a country pub he was taking her to, so she settled on her newest pair of jeans and a knitted cotton top. Remembering their trip to Franco's, she concluded that a woman's outfit was of little concern to Calum, which was all to the good when she considered her very limited wardrobe—also a bone of contention between her and her mother.

'I simply do not understand how any daughter of mine can go round looking so disreputable,' Mrs Flynn had complained more than once—on most occasions when their paths crossed, in fact. 'You're not a bad-looking girl. In fact, you could be quite pretty if only you took more trouble with your appearance...and look at you! Jumble-sale clothes! Let me take you shopping...buy you something really nice.'

Charlie was still grinning at the recollection of the endless arguments she'd had with her mother over clothes when she got back to the studio. She found Calum studying a collection of her drawings which were pinned up on the wall.

'I see what you meant when you said faces were your trade,' he commented. 'You've quite a collection here——' She moved towards him and followed his pointing finger. They were almost all portraits, sketches of her family and friends, people she'd seen in the street...all sorts.

He gazed at the drawings for a full minute without saying anything, then switched his gaze thoughtfully to Charlie. His eyes narrowed, making her heart beat painfully against her ribs as his appraising stare travelled slowly over her, almost as though he were noticing her fully for the first time.

'Very suitable—and very nice,' he murmured.

This compliment was so unexpected that Charlie found it quite disconcerting, but she had no more than a moment to register the fact before Calum stepped forward and shepherded her back through her own studio door.

'You are ready, I take it?' There was an impatience on his face that mystified Charlie. Why should he be so eager for a mere lunch date?

'Well—yes, I suppose so.' She hurried back into her bedroom for her bag and almost had to run downstairs to catch up with him.

He flung open the front door and strode off down the path leaving Charlie to lock up and follow him out to the car.

It was standing at the kerb, the brightness of its highly polished bodywork matching the shine in Charlie's eyes as Calum opened the door for her.

'I've been longing for another ride in this,' she confessed. 'I think travelling this way could become addictive.'

Calum gave a smile that might almost be called smug as he got in beside her. Charlie settled herself back in the almost indecently comfortable seat.

'I wish my mother could see me now,' she confided. 'That'd make her sit up and take notice. Not exactly Bohemian transport, is it?'

Calum laughed. 'We could call on her, if you like. No reason why not. Would you like to?'

The prospect was horrifying. 'Oh, no! I wasn't being serious!'

Mrs Flynn would certainly be impressed, her daughter thought, but the prospect of all the explaining she'd have to do, the comments and assumptions her mother would make, assessing Calum as a possible and extremely eligible son-in-law... Charlie shuddered.

'No, thank you,' she said again with increased fervour. 'I don't think it would be at all a good idea!'

'Lunch, then,' Calum said firmly, and put the car into gear.

Charlie watched the concentration settle on the clear-cut features silhouetted against the brightness of the sky, and gave a little sigh of pure contentment. She had no idea where he was taking her, but he seemed quite confident of the route.

'Do you want me to map-read?' Charlie offered. 'I'm quite an expert on the roads round Cambridge.'

Calum shook his head, eyes firmly on the road ahead. 'No, thanks. I've done my homework.'

Charlie smiled to herself. He would, wouldn't he? He was a man who liked to know where he was going in every sense of the word. No stopping to ask directions— just find out the way, and follow it.

She was no wiser about their destination when after about thirty minutes he turned off the main road along a narrow country lane.

There was no sign of a pub, a restaurant or any habitation whatever. Wherever could they be going? Charlie couldn't recall what the last signpost had said, and the countryside didn't even look familiar.

Calum grinned at the mystified expression on her face.

'Not long now. Getting hungry?'

'Hungry and curious, Calum. Do tell me where we're going.'

'I don't know that it's got a name.' He frowned as he negotiated a tight bend, then slowed the big car down. He was clearly searching for a particular spot, and at last he seemed to have found what he was looking for.

He pulled the car over on to a wide grass verge and stopped.

Charlie stared about her in astonishment. There was nothing to be seen but fields, hedges and a little copse just visible at the end of a grassy track that wound away at the edge of the meadow.

'Where...?' she began, but Calum wasn't listening. He got out of the car and went quickly round to the back.

'Come here,' he ordered her, still offering no explanation. Agog with curiosity, Charlie went round to join him. He was standing with one hand on the boot lid.

'You know I was late this morning, and kept you waiting?'

Charlie nodded slowly.

'And I never apologised or explained why?'

'You said something had come up that you didn't want to put off.'

'That's right,' he nodded. 'Well—here's that explanation. But still no apology!'

The boot flew open and, like a conjuror producing the proverbial rabbit, Calum flung out his hands.

'*Voilà, mademoiselle!* Your luncheon is served!'

Charlie was stunned into an amazed silence. This was the last thing she would have expected—and from the businesslike, unromantic Calum Sutherland of all people! She could see a wicker hamper, an assortment of cartons, an elaborate-looking cool-box and a neatly folded rug.

'A picnic!' She found her voice at last. 'You've brought a picnic!'

'You don't mind? Our family are great ones for picnics—almost a tradition, I suppose. Maybe it has something to do with the uncertain climate up there in the mists and mountains. We always feel we have to make the most of any fine day we're blessed with.'

Charlie's eyes danced as she grinned up at him. 'Now I know why you were so worried about the weather. It never clicked...I just thought we were going out to a country pub!' She peered in delight at the basket. *Fortnums?*'

'When I saw it was going to be a nice day I decided to do the thing in style.' Calum smiled with pleasure at the memory of his shopping expedition. 'I had a great time choosing everything—all hand-picked, none of your ready-assembled menus, so if there's nothing there you fancy, you can blame me.'

'You don't need to worry,' Charlie assured him happily. 'I eat almost anything, and I'm sure that——' she nodded towards the basket '—will be all a picnic should be.' She gazed round at the rural surroundings. 'Where do you intend that we have this feast?'

'Up there,' came the prompt reply as he pointed up the track she had noticed earlier.

Charlie's eyes widened. 'You've been here before?'

Calum laughed again at her bemused expression. 'No—never.'

He began lifting things out of the car and handed Charlie the rug and cool-box.

'Excuse me a minute.'

He slipped off his jacket and undid his tie, folding both carefully before stowing them away in the back of the car. Then he rolled up his shirt-sleeves—very precisely, Charlie observed, as he did everything—and something knotted itself sharply in her stomach as she noticed the golden hairs on his arms glint in the sunlight as he stretched up to pull on a sweater over his head, dark green cashmere, very soft and very expensive, like all his possessions.

She dropped her eyes quickly for fear of what they might reveal, but Calum had other things on his mind just now. He shut the boot and picked up the hamper and other boxes.

'That's better...now, let's be off.'

'How did you know where to come? You looked as though you knew the way,' Charlie asked, following him through the field gate.

'As I said, I did my homework. Actually, one of my contacts in Cambridge lives somewhere near and gave me the directions. It's a favourite spot of his family's. I hate reading maps while I'm driving, so I got the route into my head before we started out.'

The path wound slowly between meadow and hedge, rising gently, so that when they reached the little copse Charlie could see the Cambridgeshire countryside unfolding away into the distance.

'This must be the only hill for miles,' Charlie told Calum as she spread the rug on the ground. 'This is a notoriously flat county and there isn't all that much proper, old-fashioned countryside left, either. It's mostly all been ploughed up into huge, bare fields. It was very clever of your friend to find this spot...and kind of him to share it with us!'

She squatted on the rug and watched Calum as he undid the hamper, her eyes shining with childish delight as he unloaded one delicacy after another on to the plates he took from one of the other boxes.

Smoked salmon, a choice of pâtés, some cold chicken, a game pie, a dazzling array of exotic salads, then fresh rolls, butter, several cheeses...the selection seemed endless.

'We can't eat all that!' she gasped as he stood back proudly to await her reaction. 'I know I said I was hungry, but I've never seen so much food outside of a shop. You must have bought up the whole stock!'

Calum laughed, busying himself with a corkscrew. 'I decided against champagne,' he told her quite seriously. 'Not quite right for this occasion. This is a German wine. I hope you'll like it.'

'I'm sure I shall,' she said weakly, taking the glass he handed to her. Even before she'd drunk a sip she began to feel quite light-headed, this whole occasion had taken her so by surprise.

The wine was indeed quite delicious, light and somehow flowery, just right for an early summer picnic, and as for the food...

'I couldn't eat another crumb,' she asserted firmly when Calum tried to press a last helping of salad on her. 'Even starving artists have their limits, you know.'

He looked disappointed.

'I've got some dessert here—a strawberry flan. You can't stop yet.'

'Dessert...' Charlie echoed feebly.

'And coffee.'

She hugged her knees and gazed at her host in admiration.

'Do you always think of everything, Calum? Calum...' she repeated slowly and raised her eyebrows. 'It's not a common name, is it, even in Scotland?'

'A family name,' he explained. 'My grandfather was Calum, and his grandfather. The eldest son in between, like my father, is always Angus.'

'So if you have a son he'll be Angus?' Charlie leant back on her elbows and gazed with unfocused eyes into the distance. 'It must be nice, a family tradition like that.'

Calum watched the hazel eyes cloud momentarily as she thought about the brittle relationships in her own family.

'I have to find a wife first,' he said lightly, breaking the silence that had fallen between them.

Charlie brought herself back to the present—no use letting her regrets spoil such a beautiful afternoon.

'But you don't have time to consider marriage—no, I'm sorry,' she added with swift contrition, 'that was hitting below the belt.'

It was Calum's turn to stare out over the meadows. 'It's not quite true, in any case—I haven't dismissed the possibility altogether. It's just a matter of finding the right person.'

'But you haven't?' Charlie persisted, then coloured violently. 'Not that it's any of my business.'

She turned away and plucked fiercely at the grass at the edge of the rug. Whatever had come over her to ask such a thing? Calum would take offence again, and the fragile strands of friendship would be rent apart, putting their relationship right back where it had started.

She dared not meet his eyes, so was unaware of the uncharacteristic tenderness on Calum's face as he studied her bent head.

'I might have,' he said with studied casualness.

Charlie sighed and began arranging the uprooted stalks of grass into a pattern, conscious of Calum's scrutiny of her uneasy movements. What were his marriage plans to her? Nothing...nothing at all. Their relationship was only friendly, and strictly professional, and must remain so. Not that there was any likelihood of its developing into anything else, even were she to want it to...

In her confusion she became aware that Calum was speaking to her.

'There's something I've been meaning to say,' he began quietly. 'I must have sounded very insensitive, the other day, asking about your family. I didn't mean to pry.'

Charlie came back to earth. 'I didn't mind—it's just one of those things,' she replied with a rueful smile. 'You're just lucky, I guess, if you happen to get on with your family. You do, don't you? I can tell by the way you talk about them.'

'I don't think I've ever thought about it,' Calum said with a note of surprise. 'We've had our disagreements, like most families, but my parents always supported me and gave me every encouragement when I wanted to join my uncle in his bank. They never pressured me to stay.'

His eyes strayed out over the countryside so unlike the moorland landscape of his native Perthshire.

'I expect Father would have liked me to stay and help run the business—he has a small shop selling hardware...tools, nails, that sort of thing. And a grand selection of malt whiskies,' he added with a grin, 'but he could see I wanted something more challenging, and he never stood in my way.'

Charlie smiled mischievously. 'I can't see you behind a counter, even selling the best malt. And you wouldn't have got your Jag, would you?' Her smile faded as she went on, 'I suppose I have to admit my parents never actually stood in my way. They just didn't do much to encourage me. That's why I moved out to Annie and Don's.'

'They must have been pleased for you when you won the Trevelyan Prize, surely?'

'Yes, that was OK,' Charlie admitted, then laughed. 'Though Mum's reaction was pretty typical. She thought I ought to spend my prize money on some really nice clothes! And by "really nice" she meant really expensive—the sort of designer things she always wears. I must be a real disappointment to her.'

'I think I'd be very proud if I had a daughter like you. You've always known what you wanted to do and gone all out to achieve it. Like me. We have a lot in common, wouldn't you say?'

His tone was light, but a glint had come into the brown eyes, whether merely teasing or a warning of something more significant, Charlie couldn't judge. The uncertainty hovered in the air between them as he waited for her reply.

Charlie tried to turn the moment with an airy laugh which even to her ears sounded unconvincing.

'There's not much in common between a struggling artist and a highly successful tycoon, I wouldn't have thought.'

But Calum Sutherland wasn't to be put off as easily as that.

'You don't do yourself justice, Charlotte. You won't be struggling for much longer, will you? As soon as the portrait's finished, work will come flooding in. And don't forget I'm a lot older than you. By the time you're my age, who can say where you'll be? At the very top of your tree, I shouldn't wonder, and with a Jag too, if that's what you want.'

'Thanks.' Charlie smiled at him. 'It's nice to have one fan . . . oh, that reminds me. I've got something for you.'

She couldn't reach her bag from where she was sitting, and drew her legs under her to get to her feet, then fell back with a groan.

'You'll have to wait a minute, my leg's gone to sleep.' She screwed up her face and rubbed the offending limb. 'Oof—pins and needles! Sheer torture!'

Calum stretched out a long arm to retrieve the bag, then got slowly to his feet to walk round to Charlie's side of the rug. Her leg was still useless from temporary lack of circulation, and even if she'd wanted to she was powerless to move away.

Calum knelt down beside her and dropped her bag in her lap, waiting expectantly.

Charlie opened it and drew out a folder of stiffened card which she handed to him.

'Just a small souvenir,' she told him lightly, not wanting to make too much of the occasion or the gift. She watched as Calum drew out the small water-colour she'd painted of King's College Chapel rising in all its splendour from the smooth green lawns and silhouetted against the blue of a spring sky as they had seen it the week before.

Calum drew in his breath sharply. 'You did that?'

Charlie nodded. 'It's only a sketch,' she said, but Calum took no notice and brushed aside her modest disclaimers.

'It's beautiful,' he declared in admiration. 'And you painted it specially...for me?'

'I thought you might like a little reminder of King's.'

'But it's so simple,' Calum said, entranced by the painting in his hand, 'and you've captured it all, even the grandeur of the building...everything.'

At last he replaced it in its folder which he put carefully out of the way of the remains of the picnic still littering the rug.

'I shall treasure it always...and that afternoon is not the only thing it will remind me of,' he said quietly.

Charlie's head jerked back as she felt his arm steal gently round her shoulders and strong fingers warm on her cheek turning her face towards him. Then, with infinite slowness, as though he were savouring the moment to imprint it on his memory, his lips came down to brush hers in a light, butterfly kiss which made her very bones melt.

An involuntary shiver went through her and, sensing it, Calum immediately dropped his arm, twisting his head away but not quickly enough to prevent Charlie from seeing the expression of deep hurt cross his face.

'I'm sorry,' he began stiffly, but Charlie shyly caught at his hand.

'No—it wasn't...that is——'

Their eyes met and something that Calum read on the upturned face so close to his told him what she was trying to say, and his lips curved in delight as he caught her to him again.

Now the mouth that came down on hers was as hard and demanding as the hands on her shoulders, sliding down her back... She reached up to the back of his neck, to the little curls she'd noticed earlier in the studio, and she felt the auburn hair she'd longed to touch springing vibrantly beneath her fingers.

Without relinquishing his hold, and with one deft movement, Calum almost lifted her so that she found herself supported against his body with one arm encircling her waist. His head bowed to kiss the soft skin just above the neckline of her sweater and Charlie leaned back in his embrace, the edges of her mind blurring with a kind of stunned happiness.

His lips had found hers again, and instinctively she pressed against him, hardly knowing what she was doing, sensuously aware of the hard muscles of his chest beneath the soft wool of his sweater.

His arm tightened round her, then slowly, relentlessly, his hand moved upwards to find her breast, where it stayed, gentle yet possessive, making it impossible for Charlie to move, paralysed as she was by a fearful joy, in case he took the slightest tremor as a sign of withdrawal on her part.

Motionless they remained locked together, neither of them willing to break the magic spell which bound them, until Calum lifted his head just enough to look deep into Charlie's eyes.

'This wasn't planned,' he murmured. 'It really wasn't. I wouldn't like you to think . . .'

Charlie made a slight movement of her head and reached up to touch his cheek. 'I don't,' she answered simply. He caught her hand and pressed his lips into her palm, his eyes still fixed on her face as though searching for some clue to what she was really feeling.

And what *was* she feeling? Held in this man's embrace, alarmingly close to losing herself in the depths of his dark eyes, she knew this was the moment of truth, that with the slightest, most infinitesimal breath of a sign from her, the merest flicker of an eyelid, he would claim her surrender, not now, maybe, but at some time in the not so distant future.

But even as she hesitated, on the brink of letting herself fall captive to his desire, a tiny voice whispered to her from the furthest corner of her mind.

Hold back, it said. Wait.

It would be no mere brief affair, not with this man. He would pursue her with all the single-mindedness of which she knew he was capable until at last she surrendered herself, body and soul, her life and her work too, to his dominating personality and will.

Remember David, something persisted in telling her, forcing her to heed its warning against the whirlwind of emotion surging through her consciousness. You loved him, yet you managed to resist all the temptations he threw before you—don't waste all you've achieved by giving way now to a man whose very power has been bought by take-overs. Keep your independence, Charlie Flynn, don't give way, just when your career is taking off.

Still held close in his arms, with all her senses keyed-up and quivering, she was aware of these thoughts and emotions cascading through her brain to create an invisible barrier between them which the sensitive antennae of Calum's desire detected almost simultaneously.

'I'm sorry,' he said dully. 'I'd no right—it's no, isn't it?'

Charlie laid her hand on his and stared helpless up into his bleak face.

She could not bring herself to answer him directly. 'No' seemed so cruelly final, and anything else would give him an encouragement she dared not offer.

'Let's call it "not yet",' she said. 'No—please, Calum, don't look like that.'

'What use is that to me?'

The muscles beneath her fingers tensed to his touch and she gasped as he tilted her face round almost savagely to meet his lips, which came down on hers dry and hot as though he were suffering from a fever. She pressed her hands ineffectually against his chest and twisted her head away.

'I'm sorry,' she almost choked, breathless from the ferocity of his embrace. 'I wasn't expecting...I didn't know you felt anything for me, not in this way.'

Calum moved away, not far, but the gesture was significant.

'Not even after last week?' His voice was harsh.

'Last week?' Charlie pretended not to understand, although those moments in the museum, when he'd been so close to touching her, stood out in her mind with painful clarity. Of course she'd known then how he felt. Why pretend otherwise?

Without another word Calum got to his feet, releasing her as suddenly as he'd taken her in his arms, and moved away.

'I had thought...' he made a heavy movement with his hands before dropping them to his sides '...that maybe you were growing not to dislike me quite so much. But evidently I misread the signs...just now,' he ended harshly. 'I apologise. It won't happen again, I promise you.'

Charlie sat hugging her knees, watching him collect up the remains of their picnic, but in spite of the misery flooding through her she steeled herself against giving way to it—or him. It was too late now to put the clock back even a few minutes. The die had been cast.

CHAPTER EIGHT

THEY didn't speak much on the way home, and Charlie kept stealing glances at the tall, silent figure beside her. Calum's hands were steady on the wheel and the strong profile she knew so well gave nothing away.

She had to admire him. Her rebuff, although as gentle as she could make it, must have been a blow to the pride of someone so used to getting whatever he set his heart on, but his thoughts and feelings were firmly locked away behind the veiled eyes.

The true state of her own emotions she dared not even contemplate, not yet. That was for later, when she was alone.

When they drew to a halt outside her house, Charlie made no immediate move to get out.

'That was a lovely afternoon. A great treat, I can't tell you. You'd gone to so much trouble...' Hesitatingly she laid her hand on Calum's arm. 'Thank you so much for thinking of it.'

He turned to her, a half-smile playing near his lips, but his eyes were bleak.

'In spite of...?'

'In spite of nothing.' Charlie thought a moment, choosing her words with care. 'I discovered...once before...' She stopped and studied her hands intently before going on in a low voice. 'There was someone, once, but that's all finished now—for good. But I did discover then that I need my own space—independence, whatever—for a while. Until I know where I'm going...'

She tried to force a lightness into her voice but knew only too well that each word was driving a wedge into the invisible barrier between them.

There was a long silence before Calum spoke. 'It won't happen again,' he said stiffly. 'You have my word.'

They looked at one another and Charlie knew the bleakness in Calum's eyes was mirrored in her own— then the moment passed, and Calum turned to get out of the car allowing a rueful half-smile to touch his lips as he opened the boot.

'We never did have our dessert,' he said, picking up the carton containing the strawberry flan. 'You take it. You can give it to... what's your landlady's name?'

'Annie.'

'Share it with Annie and her family. It's too much for me, and anyway, I bought it for you.'

He placed it carefully in Charlie's hands and they stood on the pavement looking at one another awkwardly, each uncertain of how to say goodbye.

A wave of despair swept over Charlie as she realised that Calum had never once mentioned the portrait. Was this to be the end after all? Would he find it too painful— humiliating, even—to sit for her after what had happened back there in the spring meadow?

And there were her own emotions to consider, too, in spite of all her brave words about space and independence. Calum's embrace had aroused sensations deep within her that studying him in such close proximity would make it almost impossible to ignore or forget.

'About the portrait.' Calum's voice broke into her thoughts, and she turned wide eyes up into his face.

'There's something I was going to tell you earlier...back there...' he indicated vaguely the direction from which they'd come '...but then it didn't seem appropriate. Even now...' He shrugged and tightened his lips.

'So you are going to let me go on with it?' Charlie ventured, a seed of hope springing up in her heart.

Calum smiled grimly. 'We have an agreement, if you remember,' he said succinctly though without any great enthusiasm. 'So, about the sittings. I don't suppose you'd want me to come here again——'

Charlie flushed scarlet. 'Oh, I——'

Calum waved his hand peremptorily to forestall her interruption. 'In any case, I can't be sure of being able to come at regular intervals. I've taken enough time off recently.' His mouth snapped shut and the set of his shoulders tensed beneath the soft sweater before he went on in a flat sort of voice, 'There's a sort of studio flat in the block where I live—the new tenant isn't taking it over for two or three months, so I took the liberty of putting a deposit on it.'

'For me?' Charlie was stunned.

'You needn't live there, not if you don't want to, though it's very comfortably furnished, but you could use it as a studio and finish the painting there.' Calum studied her face intently. 'What do you think?'

Charlie gaped at him, open-mouthed. How easy it was if you had power and money. You wanted something, so you went and got it. Just like that. But she couldn't afford anywhere like that. It was hard enough even finding Annie's comparatively modest rent.

'I couldn't afford——'

But again he cut her off. 'The money's no problem. I'll pay.'

But Charlie had her pride, too.

'Of course money's a problem,' she snapped. 'I'm not in the business of accepting charity!' Her eyes fell on the box she was still holding, and she thrust it back at him. 'How would you have liked it if someone had paid your rent for you when you were just starting to make your own way? You wouldn't, would you? You'd have been too proud.' She stepped up to him and tilted her head back to glare into his face. 'Well, so am I. If that's the only way the portrait can be finished, then I'll throw it out!'

She marched past him to open the garden gate, but a hand came down on hers and Calum edged between her and the fence, cutting off her escape.

'I can't do anything, right, can I? And before you fly off the handle again, just hear me out.' He sighed and ran a hand through his hair, much as Charlie herself did when she was ruffled.

Charlie leant back against the gate and folded her arms, her mouth set in a determined line as she waited for him to continue.

'There's this studio flat,' he explained, 'a big room with a little kitchen, and a bathroom. It has large windows, facing north, which I believe is important—I asked specially. I know you couldn't afford it, but I thought you might let me pay the rent as a sort of extra fee for the painting.'

Seeing that she was about to speak, he put out his hand in a conciliatory gesture. 'I know, the commission was part of the Prize, but I don't suppose the good people who thought up the scheme considered the practicalities involved. How many Prize-winners would have a studio near their models? Very few, I imagine. So call it my contribution to the Prize.'

Charlie wrestled with her conscience, and Calum, seeing her uncertainty, added, 'Also, there's the question of the way I treated you at the beginning. I don't know how you put up with my rudeness, so I'd like to make it up to you. I do want the portrait to be a success, for both our sakes. If you accept my offer, you'll make me feel you've forgiven me...and it will save time!'

He gave her an enigmatic look and Charlie burst out laughing, breaking the tension between them.

'I can see how you got to the top, Mr Sutherland! Do you always manage to get your own way by such devious arguments?'

He gazed down at her, his expression giving nothing away. 'Always. Does that mean you accept my offer?'

'Have I a choice?'

'Of course. There is always a choice. It's what you do with it that can change the direction of your life—for good or bad.' He looked at her meaningfully, but Charlie ignored the tacit reference to the other, more significant choice she had already made that afternoon.

'You say it's in the same block as your flat...this studio?' she asked slowly. 'I do realise the convenience...'

'But you're thinking it might be a bit too convenient?' Calum was always there before her, and Charlie no longer knew whether to find it annoying or impressive.

'Charlotte, I did promise you. There'll be no strings attached—I'm not setting you up in a love-nest, if that's what's worrying you.'

Charlie blushed scarlet. 'No...I didn't...I'm sorry...'

'Look on it as a business arrangement. The portrait has to be finished. I can't come here, or not very often. The studio's available, and suitable in every way. You can't afford it—I can. It's as easy as that.'

Charlie capitulated with a grin. 'You make everything sound so simple.'

'So it is. Very logical and eminently sensible. I can't see any problem, and it'll only be for a short time, after all. Just till you finish your painting. What do you say?'

What could she have said? Charlie often wondered over the next few days while she organised the move to London. Temporary it might be, but it seemed to take as much time to sort out as any permanent change of address.

Of course Calum had been right. The studio he had found was ideal in every way. The light was good, the furnishings and decorations almost what she might have chosen for herself, and it was high enough above the city buildings to have wide-reaching views over London as spectacular as the vista from Calum's office.

'One day, when I'm rich and famous, I'll have a flat like this,' she had promised herself on the day she moved in. Calum had come to stand by her as she'd gazed through the window, but had made no move to touch her. He had thrust his hands deep into his pockets as he'd looked down at her.

'As well as a Jaguar? Do portraits pay as well as that?' he'd asked lightly.

'I shall make sure they do,' Charlie had declared firmly. 'I'm on the way to the top, you'll see.' Then she'd added on a more serious note, 'but thanks for this...' She'd made a sweeping gesture to embrace the whole flat. 'It was—is—very generous of you, and it's just perfect.'

So what was wrong? Charlie wondered despondently now as she contemplated Calum's immobile figure sitting over by her window in the big chair she'd managed to bring with her from Cambridge. She'd been here nearly two weeks, and, considering how obsessively she'd worked at the portrait since she had taken possession of the studio, it should have been almost finished by now. Instead of which...

She dabbed some paint on to the canvas and immediately wiped it off again. She wasn't doing any good and she knew it. But that wasn't only her fault. Calum might be punctilious to a fault, always arriving on time for his sittings, always perfectly polite, but he had shut himself away behind a mask of unsmiling aloofness that she simply couldn't penetrate.

Gone was the verbal sparring that had characterised their relationship in the past. Anyone seeing them together would take them for perfect strangers.

Charlie's eyes switched from the man to his likeness before her. As she had always envisaged from the first moment she'd seen him that day on the train, it was his hair that dominated the picture, but the glowing colours belied the set lines of his face, severe and lit by no answering warmth.

No longer could she glimpse any humour in the deep-set eyes that met hers, and the lines beside his mouth seemed to have become even deeper than when they had first met.

It was a powerful portrait of a powerful man, but the real man, vital, unpredictable and generous, had vanished.

Charlie sighed. If that was how he wanted her, and the world, too, to see him, so be it. She couldn't paint what wasn't there, however much she might want to.

'Something wrong?'

'What?' Charlie's head jerked up as Calum's voice broke into her thoughts. Even now he was always quick to pick up her moods, and knew her working methods well enough to understand that idle fingers meant uncertainty.

'I asked if something was wrong.'

Charlie directed a wan smile towards the easel. 'Not really wrong. It's just that it's not turning out quite as I'd intended. Nothing technical, just...' She looked across at him but met only an impassive politeness. She sighed again. There was one last possibility of getting through to the truth of his character, if it was worth trying.

'I suppose...' she began tentatively, then stopped, chewing the end of her brush with a frown.

'Come on, Charlotte,' Calum returned briskly. 'You must know well enough by now that I can't abide havering. What's on your mind?'

All this time Calum had never once invited her up to his flat, not for a meal, not even for a coffee. Not that she could blame him in the circumstances, Charlie thought sadly. So what was his reaction to her suggestion likely to be?

'I know it's not considered polite to invite oneself to someone's home,' Charlie blurted out, 'but I think it would help if I could see your flat.'

'Help?' Calum raised his eyebrows. 'Help whom?'

'Me,' Charlie said hesitantly. She waved her hand towards the easel. 'It might help me get that final extra spark of...*something*. Whatever it is that's missing. If I could just see where you lived...'

Calum stood up and turned his back to her, thrusting his hands deep into his trouser pockets. Charlie couldn't see his face, but his broad shoulders hunched with the tension she had noticed several times in the past.

'You never give up probing, do you?'

'I'm sorry,' Charlie put in quickly. 'That wasn't my intention at all. Let's leave it. I'll take a couple of days off and go back to the painting with fresh eyes. That might do the trick. Then I won't need to bother you any more.'

She didn't sound very convinced and Calum relented. 'Why not come up now, if you think it might help?' He glanced over to the easel. 'You've nearly finished, then?' He stretched, and for a moment Charlie caught a glimpse of the man she'd first met, taunting and challenging. 'What was it you said all those weeks ago when you were twisting my arm to let you paint me? Four or five sittings?'

His face relaxed at last into a smile and Charlie's spirits lifted. 'I know, I'm sorry. But it should have been finished by now, if only...'

If only you hadn't shut me out, she had been about to add, stopping herself just in time. Whose fault was that? he might have replied, edging them on to dangerous ground.

But Calum ignored the broken sentence and led the way out of the studio as Charlie grabbed for her sketch-book and followed him along to the lift, curious to discover what his front door might hide.

But Calum's flat held no surprises for her. It was almost starkly furnished, the only decoration the picture she'd painted for him of King's College, framed now and hanging on the main wall of his drawing-room.

It was a lovely flat, though, with big, well-proportioned rooms, and if it did seem rather imper-sonal, it was only what she would have expected. After all, his office had been just the same.

Calum himself gave nothing away, but merely watched her as she wandered curiously round his domain examining his furniture and few possessions—a big stereo unit, a television and video, and some books, mostly on travel or Scotland. No ornaments, and no photographs.

'You don't go in for clutter, do you?' she said at last. 'I've never seen such a room—it's almost clinical.' She gazed round in awe. 'When I think what you could do with it. All that empty wall space...you could fill it with paintings, and buy some fantastic antique furniture, oriental rugs...whatever you fancied.'

'I fancy it the way it is,' Calum replied stiffly. 'I don't like "clutter" as you call it, and I haven't the time or the inclination to indulge in unnecessary extravagances. It's not my style.'

Charlie felt chastened at the instant tone of authority. She had overstepped the mark again—how quickly he took offence at any hint of criticism. Why couldn't she remember to watch her tongue?

'I'm sorry,' she sighed. 'That was very rude of me—it's a lovely flat. It's just that whenever I see an empty wall I want to put pictures on it. Pure self-seeking, I expect!'

'And has it helped, having a good look round?' Calum asked when Charlie seemed to have come to the end of her tour of inspection. 'What dark secrets has your visit revealed that will enable you to finish the portrait?'

'To tell you the truth, I just don't know.' She caught sight of her sketch-book lying abandoned on an antique walnut table and spread her hands helplessly. 'You don't give much away, do you? Though I should have known that by now. If you could come just once more...then we'll call it a day. I've done as much as I can.'

And then it'll all be over. I'll go back to Cambridge and never see him again, Charlie thought with a surge of misery.

Calum's eyes rested enigmatically on her face and Charlie had the uncomfortable feeling he could read this disturbing thought.

'There'll be quite a gap in my life when you really have finished,' he told her lightly. 'It's been...' he paused, the lines by his mouth deepening as he sought the right words '...an interesting experience, let's say.'

Charlie's heart fell further. Was that all it had been for him? Yet she of all people had no right to expect anything else after her uncompromising rejection of him.

She followed him to the door which he held open for her without any suggestion that she might like to stay for a drink or a coffee.

'I'm sorry your visit hasn't been as helpful as you might have wished,' he said with studied politeness.

'It was kind of you to let me come,' Charlie responded with equal formality. 'Thanks.' She smiled up at him, but Calum's eyes remained obstinately veiled as he said goodbye and watched her disappear along the corridor.

Only when she was out of sight did the rigidly preserved mask drop. Calum shut his door quietly and leant against it, closing his eyes briefly. 'Finished,' he murmured to himself. 'I suppose it is...'

He stared at Charlie's water-colour and a deep sigh shook his powerful frame. A gap in his life, he'd told her...if only she knew. It would be more like a chasm, an unbridgeable chasm...

But Charlie suspected nothing of this as she made her own despondent way back to her studio. Calum's reserve now seemed more impenetrable than ever, and, as she had told him, her visit to the studio hadn't revealed anything she didn't already know. He really did seem to thrive on an existence dedicated solely to work, and find people and personal relationships just a distraction. The portrait didn't lie.

But if it didn't actually lie, neither did it tell the whole truth, and she, Charlie, had better reason to know that than any of the people who would see it.

If she were completely honest, she knew only too well that it had been she herself who had chilled the growing warmth that Calum had begun to allow into his life.

But she'd been right, hadn't she, to refuse to become involved in any relationship, at least until she had finished the portrait? She had to remain objective, and that simply wouldn't have been possible if she'd allowed anything serious to develop between her and Calum.

So why, if she was so sure she had taken the right course, did her pulses race when she heard Calum's footsteps stop outside her door, and her heart thud painfully in her chest as she watched him cross her studio to take up his position in the big chair? Why did she long to feel his hair springing beneath her fingers, and why did she wake almost nightly from disturbing dreams, yearning to recapture a fading memory of strong enfolding arms and warm lips?

Why, why, why...?

There was no answer to any of these questions unless... Yes, there was, and it pierced Charlie like an arrow. She was falling in love with Calum—it was as simple and as devastating as that.

She sat down heavily and stared with unseeing eyes out of the window as the truth swept over her. She was actually in love with him, utterly and hopelessly. He'd sworn to leave her alone, and so he had, and she'd never get a second chance to tell him how she felt about him.

There was no way she could put the clock back and say her rejection of him that afternoon in the meadow had all been a mistake. She'd lost him for good, and, the sooner she finished the portrait and made her escape back to Cambridge, the better. There she could try to put him out of her mind and get on with the rest of her life before he could make a complete take-over of her thoughts and dreams.

If only... But there was no future in 'if only' except misery and regret. Calum was a man of his word, and there was no going back.

Charlie got through the next few days as best she could, spending all her time away from the studio visiting galleries, shopping, going to the cinema—anything to try to banish all thoughts and longing for Calum from her head; and the next time he came to her studio she painted just a few token strokes, then laid down her brushes.

'That's it,' she said gruffly. She thrust her hands into the deep pocket of her overall. 'I really have finished it. There's nothing more I can do.'

A sense of loss and deprivation swept over her even as she spoke. This really was the end. She felt horribly nervous, too. What would Calum think of it? Right from the start he had resolutely refused even to glance at the canvas, but the time had come when he had to look at her work.

She watched Calum get up slowly and for the last time from the big chair and walk over to stand looking down, not at the portrait, but at her, and with such a range of expressions on the face she knew so well that she longed for her sketch-book to capture them before they vanished forever.

Surprise and relief she read, then a fleeting glimpse of something she couldn't quite catch—regret, was it? It disappeared as swiftly as it had come, but there was a question Charlie needed answering even more urgently.

'Won't you look at the portrait now?' she begged, keeping her own eyes steady on his face. 'It is yours, and you're going to have to live with it. If there's anything you don't like, now's the time to tell me.'

Charlie clasped her hands together to stop them trembling, suddenly overcome by the importance of the moment. She'd worked so hard at this painting—it had been her sole preoccupation for months, and if he refused to hang it in the boardroom, or even insisted on destroying it as Lady Churchill was supposed to have destroyed a portrait of Sir Winston...? It didn't bear thinking of. He had to like it, he had to...

The colour rushed from her cheeks and she swayed, reaching out to a chair for support as her knees buckled.

She felt a pair of strong arms go round her, lifting her from the ground as she was carried over to her divan in the corner of the room.

There was a strange gleam in the eyes that rested on her pale face as Calum laid her down gently and sat on the edge of the divan holding her cold hands in his own firm, warm ones. Charlie's heart turned over as she lay there looking up at him, powerless to resist any move he might make. He brought her fingers to his lips, then carefully laid her hands by her sides.

'Of course I'll look at the portrait,' he told her quietly, getting to his feet. 'The only reason I've kept away from it was because I was so worried I might say the wrong thing. I might have offended you, or sounded patronising. You know I don't know a lot about art,' he added with a self-deprecating smile.

He got up and walked slowly over to the easel and, watching him, Charlie suddenly realised this was as dangerous a moment for him as it was for her. He had no idea what secret depths of his character she had plumbed and revealed to the world at large. He was, after all, a very reserved man, she knew that, and any exposure of his innermost thoughts and emotions would be agony. Some extroverts might revel in the experience, but not someone like Calum.

She watched in a daze of trepidation, for both of them, as he approached the canvas, almost hearing the mental gritting of teeth as he forced himself to confront his likeness for the first time.

Even in this instant of apprehension her heart was stabbed by the realisation of just how desperately she would miss their sessions together, the excuse she had had to learn every line of his features, every nuance of colour in the auburn head which had so captivated her artistic imagination from the very moment she had first set eyes on him that day in the train.

She waited in an agony of suspense as Calum faced the easel. Did he realise that he had it in his power to destroy her with a single word? After a moment the broad shoulders dropped and he rocked back on his heels...but he remained lost in silent contemplation for what seemed like hours. Why wouldn't he say anything?

'You don't like it, do you?'

Charlie covered her eyes with her hands and drew her knees up under her chin, racked with misery. At last she heard a deep sigh from across the room.

'I had no idea...' The auburn head shook gently in wonder. 'Come here, Charlotte—please.'

Still transfixed by the painting, Calum held out his hand in a mute invitation and Charlie very slowly unwound her limbs and walked over to stand at his side. He grasped her arm and turned to face her, his eyes wide with astonishment.

'I'd no idea you were this good,' he told her bluntly, before continuing, 'Those pictures you showed me that day in the museum—how long ago it seems...' He shook his head before going on. 'I can see now, you've got that same spark here that you told me about...that spark of real individuality.' His lips curved in a wry smile. 'I don't know whether I really look like that—it's not for me to judge, but it's very sobering to find out what *you* see when you look at me!'

A glow of satisfaction began to grow inside Charlie, transforming itself into a burning flame of exhilaration. Calum *liked* it.

She tried to look at the portrait through his eyes, to see his own likeness staring directly out of the canvas at him as though it were about to speak.

It was, she had to admit privately, a bold, vibrant painting of a real human being, and, putting aside all her misgivings about what she *might* have included, Charlie knew that it was good.

She became so lost in contemplation that she didn't feel the hand move from her arm to her waist and it wasn't until Calum's arm encircled her waist that she realised, too late, what had happened.

'Pleased?'

Charlie nodded. 'I think it's nearly as good as I could have done—though it sounds rather immodest to say so.'

His arm increased its pressure, preventing any chance of escape.

'A proper sense of your own achievement isn't immodest,' Calum told her. 'And I just wouldn't believe it if you put on a maidenly simper and tried to pretend you thought it wasn't really much good. It *is* good, and you know it, so why not admit it and enjoy your success?'

He put his other hand gently on her shoulder and turned her to face him. Standing so close, she had to tilt her head back to look into his face, and she cursed herself for playing into his hands—literally—for without a moment's hesitation his lips came down on hers. She couldn't draw away even had she wanted to, and in the excitement of the moment she found herself responding with a willingness that she hadn't intended.

Calum laughed gently and enfolded her even more tightly in his arms, so that she could feel his heart beating against her breast, then with a gentle finger he tilted her chin so that he could look into her upturned face.

'Charlotte Flynn, you have achieved something which no one else on earth has ever managed to do.'

'It's not *that* good,' Charlie protested. 'What about Titian, Rembrandt——?'

'For goodness' sake, girl, I'm not talking about pictures,' Calum interrupted her, exasperated. 'I'm talking about me—and you. Never, till now, have I ever gone back on a promise, but I'm sorry; no man can hold back forever, Charlotte, except a saint, and I'm no saint, as you can see. Saints never break their promises.' He stooped to kiss her again. 'I kept my promise for as long as I could, but our contract is over now. The portrait is finished—we have no further obligations to one another.'

His tone was light, even mocking, but there was nothing light-hearted about the ferocity with which his mouth sought hers, crushing it with all the pent-up emotion he had been restraining over the past weeks.

His hands ran over her body, exploring, demanding, until Charlie's limbs felt like molten lead, threatening to give way beneath the surge of his desire.

The half-remembered sensations that had haunted her dreams flooded over her now and she knew she could no longer put up more than a token resistance against him, whatever he demanded of her.

Not that she had any desire to resist him at all, she realised with an exultant surge of joy. It wasn't too late after all—oh, Calum!

Calum felt her softness yielding to him and he gave a little laugh of delight.

'And you're not the ice maiden you've pretended to be, are you, Charlotte?' He took her by the shoulders and held her a little way away to study her face.

'Ice maiden?' Charlie echoed feebly. 'I don't...'

'Ice maiden, career woman, dedicated artist—it was a very convincing act you put on, and you almost convinced yourself too, didn't you?'

He held her gently in his arms and brushed her cheek tenderly with his lips.

'You should have known that I don't give up easily once I've set my heart on something, and this——' he kissed her lingeringly '—this is on account, and to give notice of my intentions.'

He released her then and stepped back to examine the portrait again, leaving Charlie feeling quite breathless by this sudden about-turn in his actions—and the weakness of her own protest.

'It really is so good,' he declared in renewed admiration, as though nothing out of the ordinary had just taken place. 'I think we ought to celebrate properly. Will you let me take you out to dinner? Somewhere special?'

Charlie ran her hands through her hair and shook her head. These past few minutes had left her in such a whirl she could hardly think straight.

'Franco's?' she asked. The calm atmosphere of the little Italian restaurant might be what they both needed just at the moment.

Calum looked disappointed. 'I'd hoped to take you somewhere a little grander,' he protested, but Charlie demurred.

'I don't think I could cope with anywhere grand. I'm feeling a bit wrung out, to tell you the truth, now it's dawning on me that I've actually finished it. And after...'

She waved her hands ineffectually to describe the effect Calum's sudden embrace had had on her keyed-up emotions and Calum nodded in resignation.

'Franco's it is, then. I'll give him a ring and say we'll be there in what...half an hour?' He considered her quizzically. 'It'll give us a chance to make some plans, won't it?'

'Plans?' Charlie echoed weakly. What was he up to now? 'What plans?'

'Where the portrait should be hung, whether we should have a party to launch it, who we should ask? You want as many influential people to see it, don't you? I'd have thought there was a lot to discuss.'

'Oh, those plans.'

Relief sounded clearly in Charlie's voice and Calum was quick to seize upon it.

'Why, what did you think I meant?'

Charlie spread her hands helplessly. 'You know,' she said, too exhausted to go on playing the innocent. 'Please, Calum...' She swallowed and felt her cheeks grow pink, but this had to be said. 'Please—no strings, still. You mustn't take advantage—I honestly didn't know you still felt anything for me, and I need time to think.' She smiled crookedly at him. 'You never gave any sign...'

Calum looked at her steadily. 'Only God knows how hard it's been to keep my word,' he said quietly, 'and I'm sorry if I shocked you just now, but I couldn't disguise my true feelings any longer. It's been torture seeing you, being so close, and never able to tell you——'

'Calum——'

'I know.' He reached for her hand and held it gently. 'I won't say any more, not now, or tonight. That's a promise I will keep. Tonight's for celebrating. But after...'

Their eyes met, then Calum turned and left her.

CHAPTER NINE

CHARLIE knew that if she once stopped to think about all that had happened in the last half-hour she would be lost. Emotionally and physically, too, she felt quite drained.

She stared at Calum's portrait, her thoughts whirling. Was it an affair he wanted, or something more permanent? Surely that wasn't possible...?

Stop thinking, girl, she told herself firmly. You don't know what he wants, and most likely he doesn't either. Take one moment at a time—he'll already be regretting that he got so carried away, and by the time he comes to collect you he'll be his old austere self again.

But if not... She wandered over to gaze at the now familiar view from her eyrie high over London, her fingers stealing up to touch her mouth still bruised from Calum's burning kisses.

It wouldn't take long, she knew, for her defences to crumble under repeated attacks as fierce as that. It would be only too easy to give way to his desire, matching it with an equal ardour... but what about her precious independence? He would leave her little if any of that, but she wasn't sure she cherished that any more. She wasn't sure of anything.

Fiercely she shook her head. This was the time to concentrate on the here and now, and enjoy an evening of pure celebration.

She simply couldn't cope with any added complications just now. Her work on the painting had sapped more mental energy than she'd realised.

She had a quick shower and put on her towelling bathrobe while she made up her face and decided what to wear. What about that new dress she'd bought a couple of weeks back? She'd seen it on a sale rack in a Knightsbridge boutique, dark red and slinky and much more sophisticated than anything she had in her limited wardrobe. Just right for a celebration, and it would certainly be a change from her customary garb of jeans and old shirts.

She was standing in the middle of the floor in her bra and pants when there was a sharp knock at her door.

Goodness! Was it time already? She must have spent longer mooning about than she'd thought. She would have to tell Calum to go back and wait a minute while she finished dressing.

'Hang on!' she called, pulling the robe round her again. 'I won't be a sec.'

Her hand had hardly pulled back the latch before the door was flung open, almost knocking her aside.

'Hi, Chas! Here I am again! Bad penny and all that! Well, aren't you going to give me a kiss?'

'David!' Charlie reeled back against the wall. 'What . . . what are you doing here?'

'That's no greeting for someone just come from halfway across the world to see you.'

The mocking blue eyes in the once so familiar face eyed her appraisingly. 'You were pretty hard to run to earth, I must say, I've been chasing you all over England.' His brows raised in admiration as he took in her surroundings. 'You've done pretty well for yourself since I left, haven't you?'

'It's not mine...David, what are you doing here?'

'Come to see you, as I said. The traveller returns.'

The tall, lean figure of her former lover approached her where she stood, mesmerised, backed up against the wall. 'Aren't you pleased to see me?'

Charlie stared at him, her eyes wide with ill-disguised dismay. Why should he turn up now of all times? She must get rid of him before Calum appeared to pick her up.

'Look, it's not a good time,' she began. 'I was just going out. Let's fix a date—tomorrow, perhaps?'

But David wasn't listening. Mercurial as ever, he switched his attention to the contents of the studio, lighting immediately on the canvas still in place on the easel in the centre of the room.

'Ah—what's this? Let's have a look!' He strode quickly over to it and, before Charlie could say a word, dabbed at it with his finger.

'Don't!' she cried in anguish. 'It's still wet—I've only just finished it.'

'No damage.' David swung round to grin at Charlie, then turned back to the portrait, frowning with concentration. He didn't speak for a while, then he drew in his breath in an admiring whistle.

'My goodness, Chas...that's really good. You've come on a lot, haven't you?' He bent forward to peer at it critically before straightening up again to face her, his eyes flashing with wicked humour.

'I have to hand it to you, Chas. You've got it made, and no mistake! Studios like this don't come cheap, and this is a fantastic set-up! This fellow here——' he waved his hand towards Calum's likeness '—he set you up here, I bet. Some rich tycoon, is he, providing you with board and lodging to persuade you to paint him, and offering to provide other things too, I bet?'

He ran his eyes over her robed form, then raised a hand in mock surrender. 'Only a joke,' he assured her hastily, seeing the outrage in her eyes. 'Sorry, Chas, put it down to jealousy!'

Charlie flushed scarlet. 'I think it's time you went, David. If it's of any interest to you—and it's none of your business what I do, not any more—I won the lease on this flat, and the commission to paint Ca...Mr Sutherland's portrait. Our relationship is purely professional.'

Not strictly true, but it seemed to convince David.

He pulled a rueful face. 'Sorry again—and congratulations. The Trevelyan Prize—I do know. I have my spies.'

He glanced back at Calum's face staring severely at him from the canvas.

'You've done him proud, I give you that. That's a fantastic portrait, but, my goodness, he looks a hard man. That jaw...and those cold eyes. Enough to give you a chill just looking at him.'

He turned with a mischievous smile to check on Charlie's reaction.

She refused to rise, remembering from old how he loved to say the most outrageous things just to get her worked up.

'Still, let's forget about him. Come here, you clever girl.' With one lithe step he was by her side, and he thrust his hands inside her robe, caressing the warm skin beneath as he pulled her towards him.

'Who is he, anyway?' The words were almost lost as he buried his face in her hair.

'David, leave me alone! You've no right . . . go away, now!'

She pushed against him with all her strength, clutching feverishly at the hands encircling her bare waist, but not in time.

'Calum Sutherland's the name!'

Charlie froze in David's arms and closed her eyes in anguish.

'Forgive me if I'm interrupting something,' the deep voice rasped, 'but you shouldn't leave your door open, Miss Flynn, when you're entertaining guests!'

'Oh, I'm not a guest,' David laughed. 'We're old mates, Chas and me.'

Charlie took advantage of the slackening of his hold to pull quickly away, wrapping the towelling robe tightly round her, but not before Calum's sharp eyes took in the almost naked curves of her body underneath.

He drew in his breath almost as though he'd suffered a physical blow, but David pressed on, unaware of the undercurrents of emotion swirling round him.

'No need to ask where you fit in,' he announced cheerfully and thrust out his hand. 'David Fairfax's my name. Old college friend of Charlie here—in fact, we were kind of engaged once, weren't we?'

Charlie nodded miserably, too numbed for words, and fixed Calum with eyes wide with a mute appeal which he totally disregarded.

'I imagine our dinner date's off,' he said so coldly that Charlie shivered. 'You'll want to spend the evening with your old friend, won't you?' he went on with bitter emphasis.

'Oh, don't mind me,' David hastened to assure him. 'I don't want to break anything up. I can see old Charlie any time, now I'm back—can't I?'

Charlie looked from one man to the other and even in the midst of her despair her artistic eye took over to note the sharp contrast between them. Calum, so elegantly dressed in the tailored suit he'd chosen for the portrait, everything understated yet costly testimony to the wealth his success had brought.

And David...from the split and dirty trainers to the scruffy T-shirt with its faded picture of the Sydney Opera House printed on it, beneath the top half of an old blue tracksuit he'd worn constantly even before he'd left her, he looked every inch the struggling artist without two pennies to rub together.

Both men seemed to be waiting for her response, and there was no doubt about which of them had the prior claim on her company.

She turned to Calum. 'David's just going,' she said firmly, 'and if you'll wait a minute, it won't take me long to get ready.'

But Calum had already made up his mind, and turned swiftly on his heel intent only on making his escape.

'We can discuss the plans—for the portrait—some other time,' he said shortly. 'I wouldn't dream of intruding.' He looked coolly from Charlie to David, and disappeared along the corridor.

David stared after him before shutting the door.

'Takes offence easily, doesn't he?' His lean features softened into a contrite smile. 'I'm sorry if I put my foot in it...you did say he was only a client.' He peered closely at Charlie's pinched face. 'Is he, Chas? Is he someone special?'

Charlie shrugged helplessly. 'I don't know. He wants to be, and this evening I thought...oh, David, how could you? Why did you have to come back just now? It's over, you know it is.'

David shrugged. 'I wanted to see you—how was I to know you had another fella?' He stared moodily at the portrait, leaving Charlie hugging herself in misery, but he was never one to let life's set-backs take over. His face brightened.

'Tell you what—he's obviously not going to change his mind about dinner, so why don't you come out with me?' He threw himself on to her divan and stretched lazily with his hands behind his head. 'I've come a long way to find you again—and I'm hungry!'

His blue eyes danced as they stared up at Charlie with a mock innocence she dared not trust, but she was older now, and wiser, than when they'd split up. She was tired and hungry too, and it couldn't hurt anyone if she spent just one evening, anyway, with David. At least that way she could put an end to his pestering of her.

Charlie stared at David across the restaurant table. His face was thinner and more worn than she remembered it, but his mouth was the same, quirky and mobile, and his bright blue eyes as sharply probing. There was something about them that reminded her of Calum—the same glint of humour, maybe? It was certainly the only thing the two men had in common, though.

David caught her eye. 'Still doing it?'

'Doing what?'

'Assessing people, sizing them up...see, even your fingers are twitching to get everything down on paper.'

Charlie clenched her hands and dropped them promptly on to her lap. She smiled sadly, thinking back to her first inauspicious meeting with Calum, but said nothing.

They were in a little French restaurant David had discovered in Kensington. They'd gone there by taxi, and

David was now telling her to choose whatever she liked from the very expensive menu.

'I've just sold a painting,' he told her casually. 'I did a lot of good work when I was in Oz, though I say it myself, and of course I couldn't bring it all back with me, so I left the paintings with a pal of mine who has a gallery in Melbourne, and he's managed to sell several, actually. So, eat up, my love, and we'll have a really good bottle to go with it. No expense spared!'

In spite of everything, Charlie's heart softened as she looked at him. 'You haven't changed, have you, Dave? Always the big spender.'

'No point having it if you don't enjoy it.' He reached for her hand across the table and gave it a squeeze. 'You should have come with me, Chas. Big, empty spaces, marvellous light, interesting people. It's not all beer and surf, you know.'

'But you didn't say you were going to Australia then,' Charlie reminded him. 'You were all for travelling light and making our way wherever the fancy took us...'

'I did that to begin with. Australia happened to be where I ended up.'

Their starters came, and David fell on his as though he hadn't seen food for months.

'Come on, Charlie. Tuck in.'

You couldn't be cross with David for long, Charlie realised all over again, as he regaled her with stories of his travels—racy, extraordinary stories that might well be part imagination, but which were so amusing you could forgive the embroidery.

They talked and ate and drank till they were the last customers, and reeled out into the night to catch another taxi back to Charlie's flat.

'You'll put me up, won't you?' David asked with breathtaking effrontery as he paid the taxi and watched it squeal off into the darkness. 'I haven't been able to fix myself up yet—my gear's at a mate's, but he's on the other side of London.'

Charlie burst out laughing, then pulled herself up short.

'No strings,' she told him firmly, and felt her heart turn over as she echoed the words she'd said to Calum. She'd have to explain, somehow, about David, make him understand he was nothing but an old friend. Please, God, make him believe me, she prayed urgently. It was suddenly so important...

'Too tired, love,' David was saying as they got into the lift. 'I'm suddenly jet-lagged—and with all that wine...' He gave an enormous yawn and grinned down at Charlie. 'I've missed you, you know. It was lonely going off on my own—you should have come with me. We'd have made a go of it somehow.'

Charlie shook her head and smiled to take the edge off her denial.

'It'd never have worked. Oh, it was marvellous, the two of us, but it wasn't meant to last. We'd have driven one another mad eventually.' She stood on tiptoe and wound her arms round his neck to kiss him with an almost sisterly tenderness. 'Things don't stand still, David, and I know where I'm going now.'

Charlie woke early the next morning after a fitful sleep, which was hardly surprising when she came to think of it, considering all she'd been through the day before.

She propped herself up on one elbow and stared across at the unconscious form of her former boyfriend, untidy even in his sleep. His limbs were all askew, the blankets thrown aside, and he looked very vulnerable stretched out on her floor.

She wondered what Calum would look like in similar circumstances and grinned to herself. It was hard to imagine him bundled up on someone's floor. Even when he was younger and on the way up he wouldn't have left himself without some place of his own to lay his head.

Charlie sighed. If only he hadn't come upon Dave and herself just at that particular moment...he couldn't have been expected to understand, not in all fairness. The arrival of another man on the scene would have been the last thing he would have anticipated, and just when he was on the point of taking her out to dinner to celebrate. Somehow she would have to convince him that Dave belonged to the past, a private past which was over and done with.

Clearly she wasn't going to get to sleep again. She got up and padded over to the portrait still in place on the easel. In the dim, curtained room the auburn hair seemed to glow and the penetrating eyes fix her with an enigmatic stare that was strangely disturbing.

Charlie gazed back, trying to divorce her reactions to it as a mere painting from her deeper and complicated feelings for the man himself. She thought back to David's verdict. A hard man, he'd said. Perhaps he was, after all, in spite of all he'd said to her the day before. Maybe all he really wanted was a take-over...and yet... Charlie shook her head in confusion. She still wasn't properly awake, and it was too early to try to sort her emotions into some sort of comprehensible order. Her mouth felt dry and furry after all the wine the night before—orange juice...she must have some orange juice.

She went out to the fridge, but the carton was almost empty. The more she thought about it, the greater the craving grew, and then she remembered she was out of coffee too. She'd meant to pop out to the corner shop yesterday evening, but events had rather taken charge. Still, there was nothing to stop her going now.

She pulled on her clothes and let herself quietly out of the flat. David wouldn't wake for hours yet. It was still early, but already a few people were setting off for work, and not for the first time Charlie uttered a silent prayer of gratitude that she didn't have to spend her life cooped up in an office.

She bought the orange juice, some coffee and milk and a fresh loaf in case David felt like some breakfast, and one or two other things which made her shopping bag so heavy she decided against tackling the stairs up to her flat even though the lift was soaring up to the top of the building.

She'd wait—there was no hurry. In fact, Charlie realised with a shock, she really hadn't anything definite lined up now the portrait was finished. There were various lines she wanted to pursue before she had to go back to Cambridge—drawings of local scenes, the river, that sort of thing...oh, yes, she thought happily, I'll have plenty to do now, and then when I go back...

The lift arrived and she stood aside to let the occupants out. But there was only one. Calum.

They stared at one another. Charlie gave him an uncertain smile and plunged straight in. 'I'm sorry about yesterday...it wasn't how it must have looked. Truly. David and I are just old friends.'

Calum's eyebrows shot up and he looked at her in sheer disbelief. 'Friends!' he scoffed. 'With his arms round you, and you half naked, you expect me to believe that?'

Charlie flushed. 'If it's anything to do with you, we were once more than friends—and that's been over a long time.'

Calum took one step towards her, almost menacing as he towered over her in the restricted confines of the entrance hall. His face was set and grim as he took in the bulging bag of groceries in Charlie's arms.

'He's still there, then? He slept the night with you, and now you're giving him breakfast...and you still expect me to believe it's "all over"?'

Charlie's colour deepened further, but she refused to be intimidated. 'Yes, he slept in my room. We had a meal together, and, as it was too late to get to the friend's he's staying with, I offered to put him up. On the floor.' She glared at him. 'I don't have to tell you all this. My life and my friends are my business.'

She moved to get past him and into the lift. 'And now, if you don't mind, this bag is rather heavy, and I want to get back to my flat.'

'My flat.'

'I beg your pardon?' Charlie was taken aback by the quick retort. 'Why yours?'

'The flat you live in is not yours,' Calum reminded her bluntly, his eyes cold and calculating. 'It's mine. I paid the lease on it, if you recall. And I don't rent it for you to entertain your lovers there whenever you feel the urge.'

He stood blocking her escape, and the spark of anger in Charlie's mind began to smoulder into a fire that threatened to become a conflagration.

'How dare you speak to me like that?' she blazed out. 'You have absolutely no right to be so insulting!'

The lift doors opened at that moment and some other residents emerged, eyeing the two of them curiously. Calum was quick to recover his dignity.

'I don't think this is the right place to hold a discussion of this nature,' he said coldly, reverting to his old, formal manner of speech. 'I have work to do. I'll come and see you this evening, unless you are otherwise engaged. We do have one or two matters to finalise, if you remember,' he added sarcastically.

Charlie was so angry that she felt like destroying Calum Sutherland's portrait. As it was, she banished it to a corner of the room facing the wall so that she didn't have his face staring at her all day. She made no reference to their altercation to David, who eventually surfaced halfway through the morning, but tried to put it from her mind altogether, at least until the evening when she would have to confront Calum again.

It was with quite a pang that Charlie saw David go that afternoon. She had always known that it wouldn't have worked, however hard they tried to make a go of it together. They wanted different things out of life: he was so happy-go-lucky and spendthrift, a real rolling stone at heart. He'd always had an unsettling effect on her, as did his final words to her before he left.

'I'm sorry if I spoilt things between you and your man.' The words were spoken lightly, but David's blue eyes were unusually serious as he kissed her gently. He glanced across at the portrait. 'You're a fine artist, Charlie, and obviously on the way to the top. Whatever success you have will be well-deserved...' He paused, and added softly, 'But don't forget to be a woman as well. Don't let ambition take you over.'

Hours later Charlie was still staring dismally out of the window. What did she want? Until yesterday she'd thought she'd got her future all mapped out, in her head at least. She was going to concentrate all her energies on her budding career as a portrait painter, wasn't she? That was why she'd not felt able to commit herself to any kind of a relationship with Dave or Calum either, if that was what he had really wanted.

She fidgeted around her studio, unable to settle to anything, feeling strangely flat with the departure of David and the ending of her work on the portrait.

What should she do? She felt too lethargic to go out and do any sketching. Maybe she should start packing. She could hardly expect Calum to go on paying for her to stay on here now the painting was finished...especially now.

Resentment began to burn inside her again. How dared he speak to her like that, insulting both her and David? He had no right to be so possessive. For that was what it amounted to—an overriding and possessive jealousy. He thought he owned her as well as the flat—well, he didn't, and as soon as he came to see her she would tell him so in no uncertain terms.

Maybe, though, he would have calmed down and got things into proportion...

But he hadn't. In fact, Charlie realised as soon as she went to answer his insistent knocking at her door, his temper had worsened since the morning.

'He's gone, then?' was Calum's first remark as he strode into her flat, not even waiting for her to invite him through the door.

He swept the room with angry eyes, searching for some hint of David's occupancy.

'Yes, he's gone,' Charlie replied in an even tone. She was determined to remain calm, though she knew it wouldn't be easy. Righteous anger was a difficult emotion to control, she'd discovered, and was little use as a weapon in these circumstances.

The early evening sun shone in through a side window, striking glints off the copper head like warning signals of the fire blazing within, and even now she found herself still hankering after her paints, but she tore her eyes away and wandered over to a table where she pretended to busy herself rearranging some papers.

'I suppose you've come to discuss the arrangements for the portrait?' she went on calmly. 'I don't really want to hand it over till it's dry, though.'

'Damn the portrait!' Calum's fists clenched and his eyes flashed with impatience. 'It's got nothing to do with it——' He took a step nearer Charlie, who backed away till she had the table between them, feeling the need for some kind of protection, and she stared at him, her eyes wide with trepidation as he towered over her.

'You couldn't wait, could you? Playing hard to get and all the time you were just waiting for your so-called "friend"——' he spat the word out '—to come back so you could fall straight into his arms. *His*, not mine.'

Charlie shook her head helplessly. Nothing she could say was going to pacify him, yet she couldn't let him go on working himself up into a rage like this.

'I told you, it wasn't like that——' she began, but Calum wasn't in a mood to listen.

'All the time you were involved with the painting, I held back, as you asked. Heavens, Charlotte! I thought I'd done all a man could be expected to——' He smacked one fist into his other hand in pure frustration. 'I never mentioned what I was feeling, what it was like being so close to you and wanting you so much.'

'Wanting me?' Charlie asked faintly. 'I didn't know...that is——'

'Of course you knew!' Calum rasped. 'Any woman would have known, but you chose to ignore my feelings because you were too wrapped up in your work. That's all that matters to you, isn't it? Your career, your ambition...?'

'And what's wrong with that?' Charlie was stung by the injustice of his criticism. 'It wasn't so long ago that you kept telling me that work was the most important thing in *your* life, and that you had no time for anything else.'

'That's all in the past, and you know it.' Calum shook his head impatiently. 'And at least I was honest about it. I didn't pretend I felt any other way, whereas you...' His eyes raked her coldly. 'Just stringing me along, weren't you, accepting this studio, using me as a stepping-stone for your ambition? People don't matter to you, except in so far as you can make use of them.'

'No!' Charlie cried. 'It wasn't like that—I'm not like that! You know I'm not. We were friends, or so I thought.'

'Friends! Some friend!' Calum exclaimed bitterly. 'Lord, how you must have laughed at me behind my back. Keeping poor old Calum at arm's length while you finished the portrait. Is that what you told your other *friend*—David, isn't it? And what else did you tell him?'

He had moved closer to her now, almost pinning her against the wall as he stood over her. If she made the slightest move she'd have to touch him, and that was the last thing she wanted. Charlie cowered back in an effort to make herself as small as possible.

'Didn't you tell him how the poor fool you were painting had fallen for you, that he'd offered to pay for all this——' he made a violent gesture with his arm '—and that you were keeping him dangling just long enough to be able to finish the portrait? You might reward him with a kiss or two at the end just to keep him happy...oh, I can see it all. I must have provided you with hours of amusement!'

'No, Calum.' Charlie's voice faltered in the face of his mounting rage. 'David told me all about his trip to Australia, and we talked about old times, friends...' She raised her eyes to his, willing him to believe her. 'Please, Calum—let's talk sensibly. There's no need to be jealous.'

'Jealous! Who says I'm jealous?' He emitted a hoarse laugh. 'If I'm to believe what you say, I have nothing to be jealous about, have I? You must think I'm naïve!'

Charlie felt her hands being seized in an iron grip as Calum pulled her away from the wall and dragged her across the room.

Her knees buckled as her legs came into sharp contact with the end of the divan and she fell back, powerless and limp as a doll as Calum let go of her hands.

He didn't once take his eyes off her face as he stood for a moment, hypnotising her, predator-like. Move! Charlie told herself desperately. Move now, or it will be too late!

But as if she were in a nightmare her leaden limbs refused to obey the feeble impulses from her brain, and she remained transfixed on the bed. Her eyes widened with mounting fear as, very deliberately and with agonising slowness, Calum took off his jacket and folded it carefully before placing it on a chair, and all the time his gaze never wavered. His face was calm, dispassionate even, but there was no doubt in Charlie's fevered mind as to what his intentions were.

So why didn't she escape now, while she had the opportunity? What was keeping her paralysed under his scrutiny, as powerless as a butterfly on a pin? Could it be that, deep down, beneath all her brave protestations about independence and fulfilling her ambition, all along she'd wanted him to make love to her?

No! a little voice cried out inside her as she watched the strong hands loosen the silk tie... run now, there's still time! But even as she got her legs to move in a last-ditch attempt to escape, she knew it was too late.

'I've been waiting a long time for this,' he murmured, his voice all the more dangerous for its soft, measured tone. 'A very long time.' He held Charlie in thrall in a glittering stare. 'I suppose I wasn't young enough, too staid and dull for you—and all along you were waiting for your lover to return... younger, stronger and more exciting.'

Charlie moved her head in dissent. 'No, Calum.'

'"No, Calum",' he echoed. 'I've heard that before, too often. Now it's going to be "yes, Calum".'

His mouth came swiftly down on hers, fierce and punishing, and the weight of his body crushed the breath from her as he seized her in his arms. She pushed feebly against him, almost suffocating, but his power and strength were too much for her.

She felt herself slipping into a black nightmare, losing all sense of reality... she couldn't faint, not now.

With a huge effort she twisted her head away and took a gulp of air, but the relief was only temporary.

'Look at me!' Calum commanded her, taking her chin in his pitiless fingers and forcing her to face him again. 'You were anxious enough to stare at me, "learn my face", as you put it, when it suited you. Well, now I want to look at you.'

A triumphant smile curved his lips, but his eyes were icy pools as they moved slowly to her mouth... her neck . . . and there was no tenderness in the fingers that slowly traced the path of his cold appraisal. They reached the top button of her shirt, and after only an instant's hesitation each one was slowly undone, as though he was savouring each second of his exploration of her.

His hand stopped now, and she heard him gasp as it closed over her breast, bruising the soft flesh with possessive hunger. Charlie could feel his heart pounding beneath the hard-muscled chest pinning her to the bed, and she steeled herself against even the slightest tremor which might imply acquiescence.

The bronze head was bent now as his lips sought the gentle curves cupped under his hand, and to her horror Charlie felt her stomach knot in treacherous response to the warm lips caressing her body. Her back arched sensuously, thrusting her against him even as a cry escaped her parted lips, a cry part dismay, part ecstatic acceptance that made Calum draw back quickly to search her face in astonishment.

'It was all a pretence, then?' he taunted her. 'You must have been very disappointed when I took you at your word, and all the time . . .' Calum gave a bitter laugh. 'But you can't disguise it now, can you? You're crying out for me!'

But not like this, not in anger and for all the wrong reasons, Charlie protested in a silent shout of anguish as she tried to twist away from Calum's ferocious onslaught. No longer did she know what she wanted, but one thing was certain: if she ever did come to him it must be in love. She must not submit to this violent assault—for both their sakes—or any hope of mutual respect would be lost forever.

Calum lay across her, his thighs fiercely urgent with barely repressed desire, his lips hot and demanding as they roved over her body. His hands explored and caressed and Charlie could hear his breath come in uneven gasps. 'Oh, Charlotte, come with...'

'*No!*' she shouted, and with all the strength at her command she twisted away from under him and leapt from the divan to confront his bewildered, angry stare in trembling resolve.

'You can't fool me this time, Charlotte. You don't mean it—you never have meant it. You wanted me then, I could feel it...'

Charlie held up her hands to ward him off. 'I'm not pretending, Calum, truly. Listen to me.' She caught at his hands and shook them fiercely. Surely the desperation in her voice would convince him? 'It's wrong, this way—can't you see?'

'It wasn't wrong yesterday, with David, was it?'

'Nothing happened with David. Why can't you believe me? We meant something to one another once, but yesterday...all we did was have a meal together and talk.' Charlie managed a rueful smile. 'David was jet-lagged and a bit drunk. He just collapsed in a heap on my floor—here...' She flung out her hand towards the spot where he'd lain dead to the world for almost twelve hours.

Calum caught her by the shoulders and pulled her roughly towards him again.

'Then why is this wrong?' His mouth took possession of hers once again. 'Or this?' Charlie felt his hands rove sensuously over her arms and breasts, and shuddered.

'Because you're—we're—making love—if that's what you can call it—for all the wrong reasons. You want to punish me. I don't know why...' Tears began to well up in her eyes, but she brushed them aside impatiently as she continued, 'I've never wanted to hurt you. I've tried to explain about David—but you don't want to listen. Another time, we might...'

'Might...might! That's all I ever hear! Why should I hang around, just in case one day you *might* be kind enough to accept me? I want you *now*—and here. I'm not willing to wait any longer.'

Again he crushed her lips, her eyes, her throat beneath his burning kisses, edging backwards relentlessly towards the bed.

Charlie went limp in his arms. She'd no strength left to resist.

'If you take me by force,' she said dully, 'I shall hate you for the rest of my life, and there'll be no chance for any kind of relationship between us—ever.' Not that there would be anyway, after this, but she had to get through to him. She looked up into his dark eyes and saw no pity, no tenderness. 'Is that what you want?' she asked quietly.

She stood in breathless tension, sensing his inner struggle communicating itself through the slackening grip of his fingers.

Finally, he gave a sort of shudder as his hands dropped to his sides, and he stepped back from her with lines of real pain etched on his features as the full realisation of what he had so nearly done flooded into his fevered mind.

He looked drained, his eyes almost glazed with misery, and in spite of everything Charlie longed to console him with soft words and a loving embrace. But that would be an insult. She must let him go.

Charlie drew her shirt round her and walked over to the door which she held open for him. Calum paused, searching her face with painful intensity, then left without a word. What was there to say for either of them?

Charlie watched the tall figure disappear down the corridor, heard the lift doors open and close—then, silence.

She barely slept that night as she went over and over each agonised moment of that dreadful evening, but with the first grey light of dawn she'd made up her mind. She knew now what she must do.

CHAPTER TEN

'IT'S lovely to have you back—the house just hasn't been the same without you.' Annie flung her arms round Charlie as soon as she let herself in through the front door. 'We've really missed you.'

They went out to Charlie's car together to start bringing in her things, then Annie laughed as she saw the mountain of stuff packed to the roof.

'I was going to ask whether this was just a flying visit, but I can see for myself.'

'No, I'm back for good, and I've missed you too, all of you.'

Charlie grinned, watching Annie's 'tribe' spill down the path in excitement. Annie studied her friend closely— there was a bleakness behind the smile, a drawn look at the back of the hazel eyes that Annie didn't recall noticing before.

'Too many late nights?' she asked lightly, bending down to pull out an armful of clothes from the back of the car. 'You don't look your usual bonny self, if you don't mind my saying so.'

'I don't mind.' Charlie shook her head and ran her fingers through her hair. 'Life's been a bit—well, traumatic, I suppose you'd call it—lately. But nothing being back here won't put right,' she ended cheerfully. 'I'll tell you all about it some time—but not now.'

She smiled happily up at the old rather shabby house and felt a weight of sadness ease from her spirits. This was where she belonged.

'Did you finish the portrait?' Annie asked later when Charlie was back in her old place at the kitchen table nursing a comforting cup of tea. 'Was it a success—are you pleased with it?' She stirred her own cup, keeping her eyes on Charlie's face. 'Is *he* pleased with it, your Mr Sutherland?'

Charlie's cup paused halfway to her lips. Annie saw a tremor on the lids that dropped quickly to hide the expression in her eyes. So he was the cause of the trouble—she might have guessed.

Charlie recovered quickly. 'I think he liked it. I left it there as it seemed silly to bring it all the way back, especially when I had so much other luggage.'

She gave a brittle laugh, remembering with a sharp pang of regret how she'd left the painting propped up against the divan in her studio for Calum to find. She had dropped the key with the briefest of notes through his letter-box just before she'd left that morning, and, although leaving the flat had caused her no heartache, abandoning the portrait had felt rather like leaving a child on someone's doorstep to discover and care for. So much of her had gone into its creation that she'd turned the key on it with a real physical wrench.

'You'll be going back when they hang it?' Annie persisted. 'They'll have some sort of party to launch it, won't they—like a ship?'

Charlie shrugged. 'We'll have to see.'

She stretched back in the chair and fixed Annie with a steady stare, willing her not to pursue the subject.

Annie took the hint and changed the subject, but Charlie's mind did not find it so easy to follow suit. The hanging ceremony wasn't the only ordeal that lay ahead. Someone would be getting in touch with her soon about the Young Painters Exhibition at the Hayward, and she would have to get the portrait back for that, maybe even have to contact Calum himself. Perhaps by then she would be able to face him, but for now...

She threw herself into the task of unpacking and putting her things away, but all the time her eyes and thoughts would insist on returning to the empty chair where he had sat, to the empty easel... every inch of her studio seemed pervaded by the forceful presence of Calum Sutherland.

There was no escape, either, from her memories. Even if she went out for a walk her feet would be sure to take her to those parts of Cambridge she'd visited with Calum—she could scarcely avoid passing King's College for the rest of her life.

She wondered, sadly, whether her water-colour of the chapel was still on his drawing-room wall or whether he'd taken it down and hidden it, as she had hidden away the romantic portrait she had painted of him all those months ago.

She knew where it was, that painting of him against the moorland background—it was behind a stack of other canvases in a corner of the room. But she didn't have to look at it, did she? She had nowhere else to put it, but at least it was as inaccessible as she could make it without actually destroying it, and, whatever she felt, she knew she could never bring herself to do that.

The days went by and Charlie decided she'd have to start painting again, even though she didn't really feel like it. She needed some money, apart from anything else.

It was high summer now, and tourists were pouring into Cambridge in their hundreds, so to earn her keep Charlie spent every daylight hour producing small water-colours and drawings of the colleges and other picturesque spots, which sold well enough to bring in her rent money at least.

She knew she couldn't spend the rest of her life like this. Some time she must confront all the questions that still remained unanswered, and make some sort of plans for the future.

She had developed the habit of having her supper, exhausted after a day's painting, seated in the big chair by the window where she had placed Calum for the portrait. It was sentimental and painful, but somehow every evening found her sitting there staring out at the twilit gardens.

One evening she was curled up in her usual place holding a postcard David had sent her from Paris. It was only a view of the Seine, and the message was banal enough—'Wish you were here!'—but just the sight of his handwriting was enough to open the floodgates of her thoughts.

She'd always told herself that she and David were too temperamentally opposed to be able to build a life together, but wasn't that too conveniently glib an explanation of her reluctance to build any long-term commitment, whether with Dave or with any other man— even Calum?

Had David all along been able to see past her indecision and decided to leave her when he'd finally realised she would never be willing to share her life with anyone?

The fading light reflected the misery in Charlie's heart as she heard his parting words echo through her mind— 'Don't forget to be a woman.'

It was an artist she'd set out to be, a success, nothing to do with the qualities of womanliness, whatever they might be. After Dave's departure she had decided she simply couldn't afford emotional involvements when she was building up her career. There just wasn't room in her life for anything more than her work.

Other words edged uncomfortably into her thoughts. 'Marriage is a luxury my schedule cannot afford...'

She had been shocked then by Calum's single-mindedness and what she had imagined to be the sheer naked ambition cutting him off from human contact and warmth, and now she, Charlotte Flynn, was heading off down the same lonely road.

What it all came down to was: was it worth sacrificing everything, even love, to achieve your life's ambition?

'No, of course it's not!' Charlie cried out in anguish, and if it hadn't been for David's ill-timed arrival she and Calum might even now be proving that in one another's arms.

But love's second chance had been blown away for good, and she'd never even see him again, let alone feel his arms round her, his lips on hers.

Charlie's feverish pacing brought her to the corner where Calum's other portrait was hidden, and with a trembling hand she pulled it out and placed it on the empty easel. Then she switched on the lights.

His brown eyes sought hers and it seemed to her they mirrored all the sadness and regret welling up in her heart. All that had been absent from the official portrait was here. This wasn't the cold man that David had seen—there was humour here and the warmth he had allowed to surface finally on the day of that lovely picnic, only to be rejected. Out of what? A misplaced desire for independence, and overriding ambition. That was all.

He'd promised then to keep his distance and the very fact that he'd been driven to break that promise demonstrated more than any words could have done the depth of his feelings for her, but, in the face of the towering jealousy David had aroused in him, what could she have done except reject him again?

Three small words were all it would have taken to convince him David meant nothing any more—three words she had never uttered. 'I love you'.

And now she never would be able to tell him. She would never see him again. Pride would never let him come looking for her.

But she had her pride, too. How could she go and tell him how she felt, that she realised how much she missed him and needed him?

She'd always imagined he would want to take her and her life over completely, but she had never given him the chance to prove otherwise. She gazed across at his likeness.

'I'm sorry,' she whispered. 'I'm so sorry, Calum. I love you—but it's too late. You'll never know.'

The following day, when she took the latest batch of water-colours into the gallery which sold them for her, Bill James, the owner, beckoned her into his little office.

'Sit down a minute, Charlie, if you've got the time. I want a word.'

He swept a pile of catalogues and papers off a chair and Charlie sat down obediently.

'Coffee?' Bill asked.

Charlie nodded. 'Thanks. I didn't have time for breakfast this morning. I wanted to finish something off before I brought the paintings in.'

Bill poured out two mugs and sat on the edge of his desk, considering her thoughtfully. 'I've known you a long time, Charlotte Flynn,' he said severely, 'and you don't look yourself these days.' He smiled at her affectionately, but there was no disguising the anxiety in his voice. 'There never was much of you, but I reckon you're not eating properly. Fading away, in fact. What's up, love? Family troubles?'

He knew all about Charlie's strained relationship with her parents.

Charlie shook her head, cross to feel the easy tears prick her eyelids.

'No, it's not family.'

'Well, it's not for me to pry, my love, but it won't do, you know. It won't do at all.'

Charlie looked at him helplessly and cupped the warm mug between her hands, grateful for its comfort.

'There's not much I can do about it, except go on working to forget. How've the paintings been selling?'

'Like hot cakes,' Bill told her. 'Or hamburgers—the Americans snap them up as soon as you deliver them. I can sell all you produce, but that's no way to carry on. You can do better than that, and you know it.'

'I've got to live,' Charlie said simply. 'This way I can at least earn my bread and butter.'

'Well, it's about time we added some cake,' Bill smiled. 'Listen, I'm planning a new exhibition—"Faces and Places" I'm calling it . . . work by the best local artists. And I want your prize-winning portrait and any other works you have, of course, but important ones, not just these water-colours. Try to get the punters to spend real money while they're on holiday.'

He watched her closely, seeing something he didn't understand flicker across her face, but went on doggedly, 'Of course, if you didn't want to sell the self-portrait, that'd be fine by me, but I'd still like to show it.'

'When did you plan on having this exhibition?'

'Couple of months—sooner if possible. As soon as I can organise the publicity—oh, and if you've got any spare time I'll need an extra pair of hands to help set it all up. There'd be some money in it, too.'

As they discussed Bill's plans, Charlie at last felt her spirits begin to rise. At least the exhibition would give her something really positive to think about and take her mind off all that had been troubling her...and Calum.

'I'd better be off, I suppose,' she said at last, getting reluctantly out of the chair. 'I've got some masterpieces to sort out!'

The next few weeks sped by as Charlie prepared her paintings for the exhibition. Some canvases needed framing, which she did herself with Don's help, and she even managed to produce a couple of new pictures based on sketches she'd made and never had the opportunity to work up properly.

Her own self-portrait, the one which had won the Trevelyan Prize, would be the centre-piece of her own collection, and there had been quite a lot of publicity about it and about her in the local and art Press.

'It's a pity you couldn't have shown the portrait you've just finished—the one you were commissioned to do by the sponsoring company. Who were they, again...?'

'Sutherland Associates,' Charlie answered with the old lurch in the pit of her stomach. 'It was their chairman I painted.'

'It would balance the other and show people what led from your winning the Prize. I suppose there's no chance?'

Charlie shook her head. 'I don't think so...I couldn't ask. Please, Bill, don't make me.'

Bill opened his mouth, but thought better of suggesting that he ring the company for her. Something was wrong there, and it wasn't for him to pry.

He gave her shoulders a hug. 'Now that I think of it, there wouldn't be room, anyway. Forget I mentioned it, my love.'

Her self-portrait hung in the most prestigious position in the gallery, well-lit and in full view from the entrance. No one could miss it, and it gave Charlie quite a start each time she came in. Even her parents, whom she'd invited to the private view, were impressed.

'It's really very good, darling,' her mother enthused. 'And so are your other pictures. I had no idea...' Her voice trailed away as a strangely wistful expression came into her eyes, and her tone softened. 'I'm sorry, Charlotte, I don't think I ever understood. Your father tried to explain, but I wouldn't listen.'

Charlie squeezed her mother's arm. She would never change, she knew that, but to hear these words, even once, was more than she'd ever expected, and a warm glow spread through her.

'And you look very smart, doesn't she, Frank? That outfit really suits you—though maybe the skirt is a little on the long side, don't you think? And with those flat shoes...'

Charlie burst out laughing. 'Oh, Mum, you're marvellous! Come on, have some wine and meet Bill.'

Mrs Flynn looked hurt. 'I don't know what I said that's so funny. I was only trying to help.'

'I know—it doesn't matter. I'm just happy.' She turned to her father who was studying the catalogue, sheer amazement written all over his face.

'What's up, Dad? I didn't know the catalogue was that interesting.'

Mr Flynn tapped the paper with his forefinger. 'It's the figures you artists are asking for these paintings.

Who's going to pay these sums—you can't be serious, surely?'

Charlie didn't want money talk to spoil the occasion. 'Not now, Dad. We'll discuss it later.'

But Mr Flynn was not to be put off so easily. 'Charlotte! Your self-portrait! Five thousand pounds— you must be joking, surely?' He stared at her in utter disbelief.

Charlie thrust a glass of wine into his hand. 'Here, drink this. No—I admit that wasn't a serious figure. You see, I don't really want to sell it at all, but rather than put NFS in the catalogue—not for sale,' she explained seeing the blank look, 'I thought I'd deter anyone who *might* want me on the wall by asking an astronomical figure.'

Mr Flynn shook his head in bafflement. 'Seems a funny way of going about things—still, you never know, someone might even be mad enough to pay it.'

'I suppose you wouldn't?' Charlie teased him.

'Sorry, Charlotte, not even for you! I just haven't that sort of money to spare, but I hope you find your millionaire. You've earned some luck, my love. That painting is very good.'

It had taken her parents long enough, Charlie thought with a tinge of bitterness, to understand who she was and what she was trying to achieve, but better late than never. Her spirits were further raised by her father's purchase of one of her smaller oils which was soon followed by other sales, so that after a couple of weeks she found she had sold most of the paintings on show.

During the last week, Charlie made one of her routine trips to the gallery to find Bill waiting for her in a state of high excitement.

'Look!' he ordered her, as soon as she'd crossed the threshold. 'Guess what's happened—you're never going to believe it!'

He almost dragged her to the far wall, pointing to her self-portrait, and there, on the bottom corner of the frame, was the round red sticker which denoted a sale.

'You've sold it,' he said, almost in awe.

Charlie felt the world whirl around her and she held on to Bill's arm for support. 'But who?' she asked faintly when she'd got her breath back. 'Whoever would pay all that money for an unknown artist like me?'

Bill shook his head. 'I've no idea. Jenny was here alone yesterday afternoon and someone—a woman, I think she said—rang her up and said a cheque would be in the post and on no account to let anyone else buy it.'

'And was it—the cheque, I mean? I know—it must have been Mum, though where she got the money...'

'No, it wasn't your mother,' Bill told her, 'and the cheque gave no clue either. It was a building society cheque with no covering letter. Completely anonymous.'

'I can't believe it.' Charlie clasped her hands and gazed at her own likeness in stunned silence. Then she gave a little sigh. 'Actually, I'm rather sorry. I didn't want to sell it really, or expect to. Still...five thousand pounds...'

'It'll certainly ease the pain of parting,' Bill agreed. 'With the five-thousand-pound prize money and the proceeds of all these...' he gestured to the other paintings, most of them satisfactorily decorated with red stickers '...and the five thousand pounds from your anonymous admirer, you're quite well set up.'

'Less your commission,' Charlie reminded him, pulling a face, 'but I guess I can afford that now I'm so rich! Come on, let's go and celebrate. Lunch on me,' she added with an airy wave of the hand. 'You can shut up shop just once—we'll all go, you, me and Jenny. Her eyes danced as she pulled on Bill's arm. 'Come on, call Jenny and we'll go now while I'm in an extravagant mood.' She was determined to celebrate in style.

The pavement outside the gallery was very narrow, and in her excitement Charlie danced out into the road and almost into the path of a taxi. She was only saved by a violent slamming on of brakes combined with Bill's swift action in pulling her back from the kerb.

'That was one angry man,' he told her severely. 'And I can't blame him. For goodness' sake, Charlie, be careful. I can't afford to lose my most precious asset.'

Over coffee Charlie reverted to the topic which had come up more than once during the meal.

'I've just thought,' she said eagerly. 'Someone has to come and collect the painting, haven't they? Or did the mystery woman ask for it to be sent somewhere?'

Jenny shook her head. 'No, she didn't mention anything about that.'

'Then we'll find out when the exhibition closes. Keep an eye out, won't you? I couldn't bear not to know where the picture's going.'

'You could come and give us a hand,' Bill suggested. 'It's bound to be a bit hectic, and that way you'll see for yourself. I must say I'm curious too. Anyone with that sort of money needs to be on my mailing list!'

Charlie got to the gallery early on the last day of the exhibition, anxious not to run the risk of missing the purchaser of her portrait. Also, she'd promised Bill to be there in good time to help pack up the other paintings for collection.

As he'd warned her, the day was very hectic, with a constant stream of people in and out all the time—purchasers coming to pick up the paintings they'd bought, and artists collecting their unsold works.

By late afternoon the walls were almost bare, except for one, large picture—Charlie's self-portrait.

'Perhaps it was a joke,' she suggested miserably. 'Though it can't have been, can it? No one's going to send five thousand pounds for a picture they don't mean to collect.'

'Why don't you go home?' Bill said. 'Jenny and I can tidy up and keep an eye on the painting.'

Charlie shook her head. 'No, I'll stay. Jenny, you go now. I'll keep Bill company till closing-time, because if no one does come I'll have to take it home with me.'

Jenny, who was only supposed to work part time, looked queryingly at Bill. 'Is that OK, Bill? I was planning on going out later...?'

Bill nodded. 'Yes, love, you go—and thanks for all your help.' He stretched wearily but with a satisfied smile. 'I think we can say the show was quite a success.'

It wasn't until after Jenny had left that Bill remembered he needed to post off some letters.

'I do want them to go today,' he told Charlie. 'You don't mind holding the fort if I pop out to the post office?'

Out of sight of the door, in the far corner of the gallery, was a pile of paper and string left from a spate of packing up earlier in the day. While Bill was out she could start tidying up.

Charlie got down on her knees to fold up the stiff brown paper, and as she did so she heard the doorbell ring as someone came in. Bill, probably.

'Forgotten something?' she called out. 'I'm here, round the corner tidying up.'

There was no response, though, only footsteps advancing purposefully down the gallery. Someone come to collect their pictures, Charlie thought, getting stiffly to her knees, unless...

With a little spurt of anticipation she emerged from hiding, then stopped, dumbfounded.

'Calum!'

She coloured violently before the blood rushed from her cheeks, leaving her pale and shaken. They stared at one another in disbelief, and Charlie was the first to regain her voice.

'What...what are you doing here?' she faltered, though she knew the answer even before she'd asked the question.

The brown eyes were still as compelling, the determined line of his jaw even more formidable, but he looked tired, as though the world held little joy for him.

'Did you...have you come for that?' Charlie's hand gestured weakly towards the portrait, still in pride of place on the wall facing him. 'Jenny said it was a woman's voice...'

'Judy,' Calum rasped. 'I was too busy.'

Charlie nodded. He hadn't been too busy, she was certain, but however much he had wanted the portrait he could not have brought himself to ask for it.

Their eyes met in misery, but neither had the courage to make the first move.

'Shall I wrap it for you?' Charlie asked at last. 'I've got all the stuff here.' She pointed to the brown paper still in a heap at her feet.

Calum shook his head impatiently. 'No, I'll take it as it is.'

Charlie moved across to unhook it from the wall. 'It was a lot of money,' she commented quietly. 'I'm sorry—I wasn't sure whether I really wanted to sell it.'

She lifted the portrait down and stood it on the floor between them, resting her hands on the frame. 'I don't understand why, after...after all that happened,' she faltered.

'It was all I could have, wasn't it?' Calum's voice was harsh, and there was real pain in the eyes Charlie forced herself to meet. 'I knew it was all over—the way I behaved was unforgivable. I've been too ashamed even to try to tell you how I felt—and then I saw this. I thought if I bought it...I didn't mean you to find out it was me...it would be—oh, I don't know,' he ran his hands over his face, 'a sort of recompense, I suppose. And at least I'd have something of you.' Then something of the old familiar fire glinted in his eyes. 'But *you* didn't waste much time, did you?'

Charlie retreated, bewildered by his sudden attack. 'What d'you mean?'

'I saw you, dancing along with your boyfriend. Too taken up with him even to notice when I almost ran you over.'

'Ran...it was *you*? In the taxi?'

He nodded.

'That wasn't...oh, Calum, I can explain all that!'

But Calum shook his head, and picked up the portrait in his arms. 'You explained before, about David. I almost believed you—heaven knows I wanted to—and after you'd left I convinced myself you'd been telling me the truth after all, which was why I wanted this... But that afternoon last week, when I saw you looking up at that man...'

The gallery door opened and Bill breezed in.

'Oh, good,' he said, seeing Calum holding the portrait. 'You've come for Charlie's portrait . . . this is the artist, by the way . . .' He rested his hand on her shoulder and went on, 'We've all been a bit puzzled about who had bought it.'

He smiled at Calum who, so far as he was aware, was a complete stranger. 'Are you taking it like that, or would you like it packed? I'll do it, love—you must be worn out after all the excitement.'

He smiled down at her but she looked at him in despair.

'Please, Bill—could you leave us alone for a moment? I'll explain later.' She seemed to be fated to explain one man in her life to another.

Bill looked from Charlie to Calum and back again. 'You OK, Charlie?'

'Yes, Bill, I'm fine. Please . . .' There was real anguish in her voice and Bill nodded reluctantly.

'I'll be in the office if you need me,' he said with a warning note, then disappeared, leaving them alone.

There were two hard chairs abandoned in the middle of the gallery and Charlie took the portrait from Calum, propped it against the wall and dragged the chairs across, motioning Calum to one of them.

Sitting facing one another in the empty room they must have looked very funny, Charlie thought, but she for one didn't feel like laughing, and one glance at Calum's set features told her he didn't either.

She pulled her chair nearer and leant forward to grasp his hands. It was now or never, and one of them had to cross their self-imposed barrier if he wasn't to walk out of her life forever, this complex, proud and passionate man. And she'd thought him so cold, once.

'Listen, Calum,' she said urgently, as she'd said what seemed like centuries ago when she had tried to explain what painting meant to her.

The strong fingers tightened round hers almost painfully, but Charlie didn't draw away. One false move and everything would be lost.

'Bill is a friend—and only a friend. He has never been anything else. He owns this gallery and has been very generous to me over the years, showing and selling my work, and employing me when times were hard. I owe him a lot, and I'm very fond of him. When you saw us together last week I was taking him and his assistant, Jenny, out to lunch to celebrate my selling that...to you, as it turned out!'

Her lips curved in an ironic smile as she fixed her eyes, wide and clear, on Calum's face, and he nodded slowly.

'As for David,' she went on, 'everything I told you about him—about us—was true. Whatever else you may think of me, I am not a liar. If he'd slept with me that night I'd have told you.'

He nodded again, and waited, not speaking, for her to continue.

'He was...we were close once, but that was a long time ago, a very long time. I guess we're still fond of one another—you can't just turn affection on and off like a tap—but we...I...' Charlie faltered, but she forced herself to go on. 'I was determined to make my own way as a painter. I'm sure Dave will be successful, too, but in a different way. As you said, he goes for the Bohemian lifestyle, but I seem to need a more settled existence. Conventional, even.'

She smiled again in gentle self-mockery, but the memory of David's final words to her erased the smile quickly from her face. 'At least, that's what I told myself then.'

Such a long silence followed that Calum was forced to speak.

'You don't think that now?'

'I...I'm not sure,' Charlie confessed wretchedly. 'I've been doing a lot of hard thinking lately, and been looking at myself pretty closely.' She nodded over towards the self-portrait. 'It doesn't tell it all, does it? I left out the selfishness and the hard, ruthless emotion that drives people away. She's not a nice girl at all, that girl in the portrait, and she deserves to be lonely.'

Her voice broke as she stared at Calum in misery.

Calum placed her hands gently on her lap and got to his feet to crouch down in front of the painting.

'I don't see any of those things,' he said softly, not looking at Charlie but at the canvas before him. 'I see only fierce determination to make the most of the talents she was blessed with. I see courage, honesty and a proper pride in her own achievement. Don't forget I've been taught by an expert what to look for in a portrait...I also see,' he went on in a different, husky voice, quite unlike his usual forthright tones, 'eyes I never tire of looking into, a mouth made for kissing—and the body of a loving, passionate woman...a woman I never knew how much I missed or wanted or loved until she went away.'

His auburn head was turned away, but gleamed like a beacon of his emotions under the spotlight high on the wall. Her eyes shining with unshed tears, Charlie took a step towards him—and that was all it needed.

With a swift movement Calum seized her in his arms, covering her face, her hands, her neck with kisses.

'My love,' he said simply, 'my dearest love.'

A wild joy such as she'd never imagined possible swept over Charlie, overwhelming her utterly, as she thrust her fingers through the springing, copper hair and pulled his head down, matching the ferocity of his kisses with an answering passion that left her gasping for breath.

Calum ran his warm hands lightly down her arms and over her breasts, making her shudder with ecstasy, but now there was a gentleness in his eyes Charlie had never seen before.

She caught at his hand and pressed it to her lips, all pride swept away by a rising flood of emotion swelling her heart until she thought it would burst.

'I've missed you so much,' she told him softly. 'I never knew what it would be like, really needing someone. I need *you*, Calum, and I can't live without you.' She paused and added shyly, 'I love you, you see.'

Calum gave a shout of exultant laughter which reached Bill in his office.

Puzzled, he put his head out of the door. 'What . . .?' he began, but the sight of the two rapturous faces was enough to tell him all he needed to know, and he went back to his desk with a resigned smile. He had a lot of paperwork to catch up on, after all . . .

'My dearest, darling Charlotte.' Calum caught her to him again and held her tight against him. Then he tilted her chin with a gentle finger and looked into her eyes with sudden gravity. 'There are two things I still need to ask you. One thing depends on the other—and I want you to think very carefully before you answer.'

Charlie nodded, her breath coming fast and unevenly as her heart thudded painfully against his broad chest.

'Will you be my wife? And before you say any-thing . . .' he placed his finger against her lips '. . . I want to promise I'll give you all the space, as you put it, and the time, and the support you need for your work. I know how much it means to you, and I'll be very proud to be able to share in it—if you'll let me?'

Tremulously Charlie's lips formed the word 'yes' but no sound came. This seemed enough to satisfy Calum, though, as his face lit up with a boyish grin.

'So,' he said smugly, 'to my second question. Do you think King's College would lend us their chapel for the ceremony?'

'I shouldn't think so for a moment.' Charlie was shocked at the very suggestion, but as she leant against him, cradled in his arms, she wondered. With a man like Calum Sutherland, anything was possible!

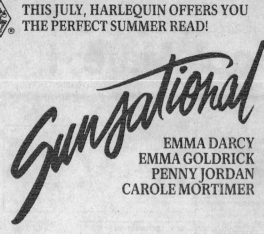

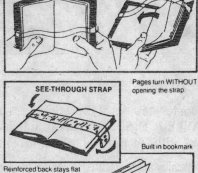

Back by Popular Demand

Janet Dailey
Americana

A romantic tour of America through fifty favorite Harlequin
Presents, each set in a different state researched by Janet
and her husband, Bill. A journey of a lifetime in one
cherished collection.

In August, don't miss the exciting states featured in:

Title #13 — ILLINOIS
The Lyon's Share

#14 — INDIANA
The Indy Man

Available wherever
Harlequin books are sold.

This August, don't miss an exclusive
two-in-one collection of earlier love stories

MAN WITH A PAST

TRUE COLORS

by one of today's hottest
romance authors,

Jayne Ann Krentz

Now, two of Jayne Ann Krentz's most loved books are
available together in this special edition that new and
longtime fans will want to add to their bookshelves.

Let Jayne Ann Krentz capture your hearts with the love
stories, MAN WITH A PAST and TRUE COLORS.

And in October, watch for the second two-in-one
collection by Barbara Delinsky!

Available wherever Harlequin books are sold.